PILO TRAIN SERIE

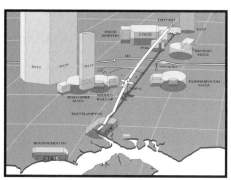

PRACTICAL NAVIGATION

A step-by-step guide to flight planning and navigation
for both students and experienced pilots.

MARTYN SMITH ATPL BSc

ISBN 1 901750 03 5

Published by the Pilot Training Centre.
Distributed by ASCO, Old Hospital, Aldbury, Tring, Herts. HP23 5SF, U.K.

PILOT TRAINING CENTRE

For my loving wife, Julie, whose encouragement

is my inspiration and for Hayley and the twins, Ryan and Lorna.

Maybe one of the three will follow their Daddy into flying....

PREFACE

Another text book about navigation? This one's a bit different. Firstly, it is not a dry, academic tome designed solely with your navigation examination in mind and secondly, it is written entirely around one specific flight. You will be taken from the flights' inception at the planning stage, right through to its' conclusion as though you had flown it yourself. Along the way, you will encounter all sorts of problems and navigational theories and these will be addressed as they are met. At the end of all of this, you might even be a half reasonable visual navigator!

I have tried to keep the tone 'light' and friendly as though we were having a one to one chat about flying and I have tried, where possible to throw in personal experience to illustrate my ideas. I have found that the people I have taught learned better this way.

This book is not only for students, either! It is also meant to be a good revision aide for PPLs who feel in need of a further bit of study - and who doesn't, where flying is concerned?

Also by the same author :-

Diversion Planning
.....or how to navigate around the world using just a stopwatch and pencil.

YOU WILL NEED THE FOLLOWING ITEMS :-

1:500 000 Southern England Chart

Protractor

Ruler (Scale)

Chinagraph pencil

CRP 1 or 5 Navigation Computer
(or equivalent)

PRACTICAL NAVIGATION

Navigation represents the first practical use that you will have for an aeroplane. That is in going from point A to point B. Although the actual process of flying to a destination sounds a little complicated, the difficult bits are really accomplished prior to flight and provided that the pre-flight planning has gone well then the actual airborne bit is simply a matter of straight and level flight on a particular heading and altitude, with a little radio work thrown in. Occasionally you will be called on to make a few simple calculations and alterations to your plan whilst actually in the air but careful work prior to departure should minimise any difficulties here.

The best approach to take with navigation is a systematic one and so we will have to develop a system that is easy to operate and fairly quick to use so that, once planned, you will have plenty of time to devote to studying your route. And believe you me with a little practice, a good plan and some care in pre flight planning then you can consistently hit targets to within an accuracy of a few seconds! Who needs their GPS?!

Since we are talking here about practical applications then I am going to begin with a practical stance rather than a theoretical one, although we will of course delve into theory when required.

So, we had better start planning! Some of you reading this will no doubt be learning to fly from small airfields outside of what we term 'controlled airspace' and some of you will be operating from within it. I would like to cater for both scenarios so we will plan our route to start from Southampton, whose airspace is controlled and we will aim for Oxford, whose airspace is not. By doing it this way, we can make some interesting comparisons between the way each airfield works.

Let's get our hands dirty so to speak and grab an aeronautical chart. Most light aeroplane pilots work off of what we call the 'half-mill' chart or the 1:500,000 Southern England chart. The numbers are really a reference to the scale of the chart. Looks a bit of a nightmare to start with, doesn't it? How on earth are you going to navigate off that, with all of those coloured and shaded areas and what do all those lines and numbers mean? Well, that's a very good question and the answer is not easy! There is no substitute for getting out your aviation law book and grabbing your instructor to go over with you exactly what all of the deliniations on the chart mean. There is also a pretty comprehensive key at the base of the chart and this should again be consulted and studied.

▶ PROJECT

Familiarise yourself with the following:- ATZ; MATZ; ASR; Danger Area; Prohibited Area; Restricted Area; Controlled Airspace Class A to G; Airways; TMA. Use a book and/or an instructor to help. Learn the abbreviations; make use of an aviation law book and revise your knowledge of air law.

Any navigation exercise (or 'navex') must first obviously start with the drawing of your intended route on the chart. However, before we do this, let's take a look at what we mean by the term 'controlled airspace' at Southampton and at its' consequences to us as visual flying rules (VFR) pilots.

Southampton has a reasonable number of airliners and other scheduled instrument flight rules (IFR) traffic both arriving and departing. This traffic requires separation both vertically and horizontally from all other traffic for safety. The easiest way of providing the requisite separation from 'other traffic' is to keep the 'other traffic' out of the way! We, as VFR or visual flight rules pilots, constitute the 'other traffic' and thus we are subjected to certain controls from air traffic control (ATC). In practice, this 'control' amounts to very little - you will be told to depart or arrive at the controlled airspace boundary at certain points, not above a specific altitude and with a visibility restriction. By giving you these restrictions, the IFR traffic can then be separated from the VFR traffic allowing everyone to fly a little more safely.

To give you a working analogy for the Southampton control zone, consider it to be a safari park! (See diagram 1). The zone boundary drawn on your chart is thus represented by the park fence. Let the IFR traffic be the lions contained within, leaving ATC the job of park wardens! Now the major difference between a zoo and a safari park is that you can drive into a safari park. Thus the VFR pilots become the visiting public. To enter a safari park you arrive at a particular gate and you depart by another, driving in between the two on designated tracks with speed restrictions. These gates therefore represent the control zone entry/exit points, known as visual reporting points or VRP's and the tracks are synonymous with your zone exit clearance . Again, flying in a zone has visibility restrictions the same as driving in a park has speed restrictions.

Now providing that you do not get out of your car, then you will not be eaten by the lions, so providing you fly as per your clearance in the zone, then you will not be 'lunched' by any marauding Jetstreams or Fokker Friendships!

(Incidentally, the park entrance fee must therefore be analogous to a landing fee!)

So having thus determined that flying in controlled airspace is no more or no less

Diagram 1

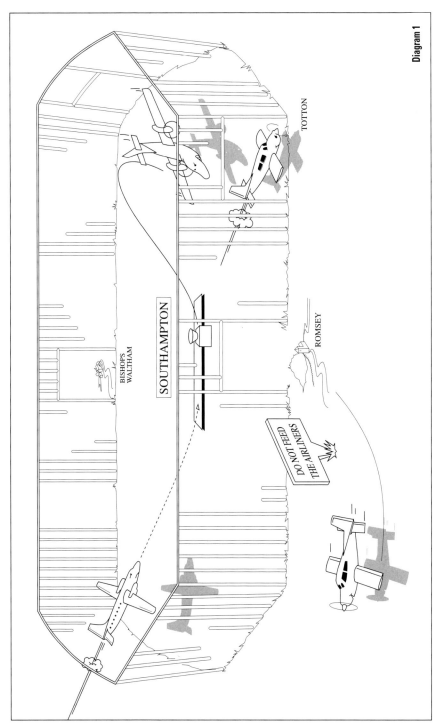

difficult than going to the zoo, (or as our American friends would put it - " its just a walk in the park! ") let's consider the implications of all of this on our planning.

We have established that you will be required to depart Southamptons' controlled airspace at certain points. (VRP's, remember?). So it's not going to be a good idea drawing your route from OVERHEAD Southampton. Rather it would be more sensible to draw it from a VRP in use or from an obvious geographic landmark. You can end your route on your chart directly overhead Oxford aerodrome however, because Oxford does not have any controlled airspace. Obviously if Southampton lay in uncontrolled airspace then you could depart either 'on track' or from the overhead.

Oxford lies to the north of Southampton so, ideally, you would consider using a northerly VRP as your point to plan from. Recently however, the northerly VRP's at Southampton have been withdrawn. The two VRP's that you might exit the zone from are thus Bishops Waltham or Romsey, lying to the east and west of the airfield respectively. Obviously using these will increase your track miles flown and so the smart money lies with you asking to leave to the north but being aware of the possibility of having to initially go to a VRP, depending on the traffic within the zone. Plan to start your navigation at an obvious point outside of the zone to the north, which is also readily accessible from either of the two previously mentioned VRP's. That way you have covered all of the likely scenarios.

If you look at the section of the chart reproduced overleaf, you will notice that I have indeed picked out a town just outside of the Southampton control zone (zones extend from the surface to a specified altitude) just to the north of Winchester.

Now you can draw in your route (track). The town that I have started from is actually called Kingsworthy, the name coming from my local area knowledge, as it is not named on the chart. It is the town shown just below the words "Solent CTA 2000 - FL55". From Kingsworthy I have drawn a straight line in chinagraph pencil, straight to the overhead at Oxford. This is the line that you are planning to fly and is called your track. Remember this!! Your track is the line on your chart that you wish to fly.

Sometimes when you draw your track line on your chart, it will run across some airspace like a danger area for example, over which it would be hazardous or even illegal to fly. Or it might run through an aerodrome traffic zone (ATZ), cross a military ATZ (MATZ) or even enter controlled airspace (the zoos, remember!).

Now the beauty of flight as a form of transport lies in its inherent ability to route 'as the crow flies' or put in simpler terms we can fly direct to our destination. ALL airspace can be flown around, over, under or even, by negotiation, through, so the obvious thing to do is to draw your track direct to your destination and then take

U.K. 1:500,000 CHART SECTION

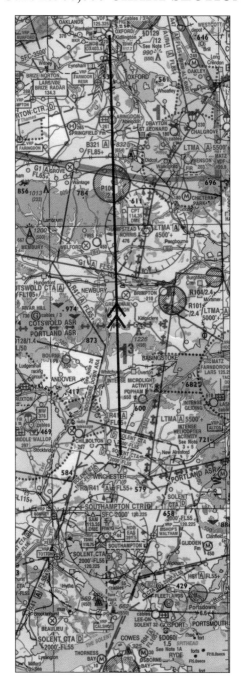

steps to assess what you have to do when airspace problems arise. In other words, assume that you can route direct towards your target (well, some of you might one day be military pilots!!) and then work backwards to see if there really is a problem with airspace and if so, what are you going to do about it?

Our track clears a control area, brushes close to a MATZ, crosses an altimeter setting region (ASR) boundary, runs overhead an ATZ (now shown as a disused aerodrome), through a prohibited area, comes close to another MATZ, overflies an ATZ and 'burgles' a CTR before finally coming to rest at Oxford Kidlington. Wow!! Incidentally the control area is abbreviated 'CTA' and is basically a box of controlled airspace running from one altitude or flight level to another. Just think of it as a piece of airspace floating in the sky, as opposed to a zone which sits on the ground.

The above route is enough to give the average student nightmares and to cause PPL's (licence holders) to change their destinations! Or is it? Compare our track as previously described with the three dimensional picture overleaf. An important area for you to work on when looking at your chart is the situational awareness with respect to the vertical. You need to be able to visualise the vertical extent of airspace by looking at your chart. Yes, there is a lot of airspace to negotiate on our trip to Oxford and yes, it could take a lot of radio work to talk our way through it. But remember that you can always go under, through or even above most airspace. Why sacrifice our one great advantage of travel as the crow flies? The three dimensional depiction of our route shows an aeroplane clearing the Southampton CTR and CTA, (CTA not drawn for reasons of clarity) climbing to an altitude at which it could overfly all of the previously mentioned airspace items and that need only be 3,500 feet above mean sea level (AMSL).

▶ PROJECT

Bearing in mind your last task, which was to learn to identify the different types of airspace on your chart and having drawn in your track line on the chart from Kingsworthy direct to Oxford, study the route with your new found knowledge. Pay particular attention to the upper limits of each type of airspace that you encounter along your track and satisfy yourself that at 3,500 feet above sea level, you do indeed clear everything. When you begin to start planning routes that you actually fly, you will realise that the preparation does take a lot of time and that it cannot be rushed if the trip is to be a success. Successful flights result in less money spent overall on training, so do not skimp on pre-flight preparation. In fact, take a tip and split your planning into two distinct phases- 'advanced' preparation; which can be accomplished many days prior and 'on the day' preparation; which hinges on the use of up to the minute meteorological data and can therefore only be realised immediately before flight.

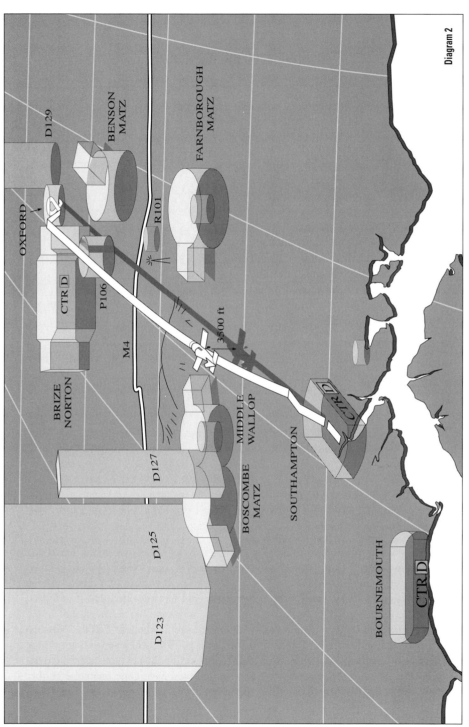

Diagram 2

ADVANCED PREPARATION

We have already begun the former, the advanced 'prep', by drawing in your track line and studying the route. Both types of prep take the form of noting down data, on which navigational calculations are performed and so we need a sheet of paper in order to do this, which is called a "Plog" or pilot's log. I have included a blank copy of the plog that I use, although of course there are many different types available. Remove it or photocopy it for use as you follow the plan in this book. When you mark in the advance prep on your plog for the first time, I suggest that you use, say, a blue pen and then compile the 'on the day' prep in red so that in looking back on your planning processes, the two areas can be differentiated. As we progress through the planning, you will need to fill in your plog. I have included both partially and fully completed plogs in this book so that you are able to check as you go that you are filling in the details correctly and in the correct spaces. You should thus follow my text and conduct your own plan alongside of my own, checking as you go that you are correct, by referring to the partially completed plogs that I have included throughout the text. Although Southampton to Oxford proves to be a short trip, much is packed in!

We will use G-OPTC, an AA5 A 'Cheetah' to fly our trip from Southampton to land away at Oxford. Unless you actually fly the AA5 then you will need to know a little about it; such as the fact that it cruises at 90 knots (kts) indicated airspeed (more about that later) and that it will burn approximately seven gallons of avgas per hour at this speed.

Turning to our plog, (page 22) then straight away you can see that we can fill in both the aircrafts' callsign and the pilots' name. Further, we have also recorded the fact that we wish to obtain both the 2,000´ and 5,000´ winds and temperatures. There is a column nearby headed 'IAS' and this stands for Indicated Air Speed. IAS is the speed that is shown to the pilot, in flight, on his airspeed indicator. 90 kts has been entered in this column. We will come back to the subject of speed a little later, suffice to say it gets a little more complicated than I am letting on at present!

The main area of interest on the plog is in the row of columns marked 'from' and 'to'. Here you are going to record your route details and should begin doing so by writing in from KINGSWORTHY to OXFORD. The track has already been depicted on the chart and I hope that by now you have decided that it is indeed possible to fly the direct track to Oxford. As navigators, we are interested in the direction of our track, which we will note in the column labelled 'Trk(T)'. Now the fundamental reference for direction is the north pole. If, wherever you are on the surface of the earth, you point to, or look at, the north pole then you have found the direction of north. True north, we call it. In fact you have gone one stage further because you have also found true south since this is simply defined as being opposite to true north. What a beautiful concept - north and south as yet uncorrupted by variation and deviation! Sorry! I only threw that in to give you a taster for what was to come!

The track direction is the angle between the north reference and the track itself. This is very straightforward to measure on the chart using a protractor, although I could open a can of worms here if I am not too careful! In fact, to avoid doing so early on in the game, I am going to give you a simple rule that you should take to heart. Please always apply this rule for which I promise an explanation later on. The rule is very simple. When you are planning to fly, then you will measure the track direction at or about its' midpoint. It is not particularly important if you are travelling essentially north or southwards but is essential for flight east or westwards. Hang on, what is east or west? Well, east is the direction in which the earth is rotating and west is opposite to this. Clever, eh? Appendix (1) is the fount of all knowledge with respect to this problem.

The actual act of measuring the track direction is best explained with the aid of diagram 3 (below) but simply involves placing the protractor on the chart so that the centre hole lies on the track line. Now you will have to align the instrument with the direction of true north and this is achieved by turning the protractor so that any of the parallel lines marked on it are parallel to the vertical lines running up and down the chart.

These vertical lines are called meridians and run between the two poles, defining true north and south.

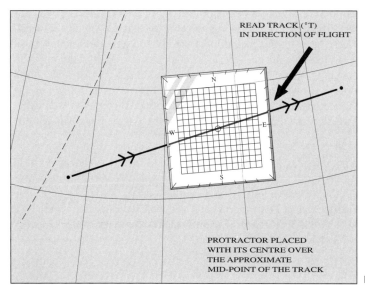

READ TRACK (°T)
IN DIRECTION OF FLIGHT

PROTRACTOR PLACED
WITH ITS CENTRE OVER
THE APPROXIMATE
MID-POINT OF THE TRACK

Diagram 3

▶ PROJECT

Having read the text on how to measure the track direction and observed the diagram take your protractor and measure the track angle. Remember that as we are going essentially northwards in this case then you can ignore our previous rule. Once you have done this then you can begin compiling a plog.

Hopefully you will have confirmed my measurement of a direction of 359 degrees true. (By convention, direction is always given as a three digit grouping, so a track of 7 degrees is said as 'zero zero seven'. This avoids any chance then of error occurring if a direction was passed to you on the radio.)

Immediately following the track column, there are two columns for drift and heading. We cannot do anything with these until we have the relevant meteorological data (met data) and so leave these blank for the time being. The very next column though, is headed 'Var' and this stands for variation. Variation is concerned with our previous study on direction but we must first cover a little more theory.

On board our light aeroplane there is nothing that seeks out the direction of true north and hence we cannot fly true directions. Instead, we have a compass to define our reference for direction. A compass works by seeking out the magnetic field lines from the earths' magnetic field. This field is due to molten magma flowing inside the earths core (sounds a little like geology to me and since I am, by trade, a flying instructor I shall leave it at that!). We can thus think of the earth as a sphere (it's actually an Oblate Spheroid which is a posh term meaning a slightly flattened sphere) with a very large bar magnet at its centre. In an ideal world, this magnet would have been aligned with the spin axis, or polar axis, so that the compass needle, in responding to the magnetic field lines, would have pointed to the north pole or true north. However, in practice, our model of the earth falls down on the grounds that the magma that I mentioned is in a state of flux and so we have a magnetic field which is not only mis-aligned with respect to the polar axis but it is also moving!

We therefore bring into play the idea that there is a MAGNETIC NORTH POLE in addition to the true north pole. This magnetic north pole is currently somewhere over Hudson Bay. So, wherever you are on the earths' surface if you look at the true north pole you are looking at TRUE north but if you look at the magnetic north pole you are looking at MAGNETIC north. The difference between the two is known as VARIATION. (See diagram 4).

VARIATION BETWEEN TRUE AND MAGNETIC NORTH.

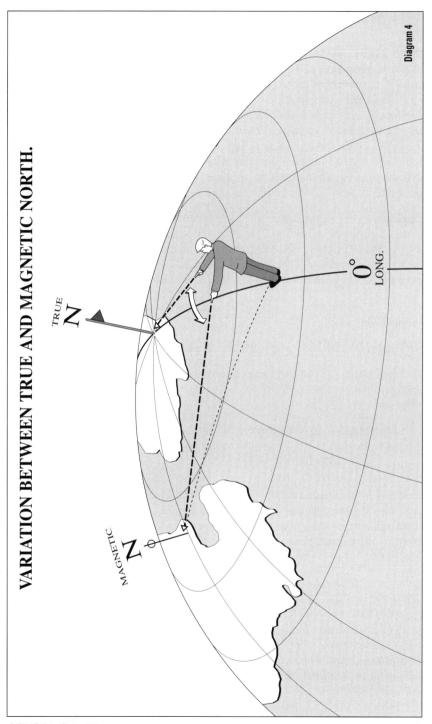

Diagram 4

To be a little more precise, variation is the angular difference between true and magnetic north measured at your current position. 'Mag' north as it is known lies either to the WEST or to the EAST of true north. The amount of variation depends on your current position on the earth's surface. Fortunately for us as navigators, somebody has taken both the time and trouble to 'map' out the earths' variation and this has been done by marking in the lines of equal magnetic variation. These lines are called ISOGONALS. There is one 'special case' isogonal called an AGONIC LINE which is the isogonal depicting zero magnetic variation. (You will not need to know this; I only throw this one in should you appear on 'University Challenge' or 'Strike it Lucky'. Don't laugh - I appeared on the Challenge three times!)

Isogonals appear on your chart as reddish dotted lines and if you follow them down to the southern end or bottom of the chart you will see that they are marked, eg 4 $\frac{1}{2}$ degrees west. It follows that if you have measured the true track direction and you have westerly variation, then the magnetic track direction is actually BIGGER than the true one. Diagram 5 will help (overleaf).

We can utilise a simple rhyme here to illustrate the difference between true and magnetic directions :-

"Variation WEST, Magnetic is BEST", "Variation EAST, Magnetic is LEAST"

In other words, if you are currently experiencing westerly variation then the magnetic direction EXCEEDS the true direction by an amount equal to the variation :-

Track is 359° True with 5°W variation.

The magnetic track is thus 004°.

Studying the chart near Southampton shows that the local isogonal is the 4$\frac{1}{2}$degrees west line and that this lies to the west of our track. In fact, further investigation reveals that the isogonals increase to the west thus as we generally deal in whole figures, then it would be sensible to round down the variation locally to 4°W. Mark this on the plog.

Ignore all of the columns marked 'Hdg (M)', 'Dev' and 'Hdg (C)' as these are again dependent on a knowledge of the prevailing met data. Instead, look at the column headed 'Dist'. This stands for 'distance' and is measured in nautical miles. Use a scale ruler in order to measure this but do please be careful that you are using the correct scale for your chart! (1:500,000). The scale, incidentally, is merely the ratio of a distance on your chart to the equivalent distance on the earths surface. Thus a line of one inch in length drawn on your chart will represent 500,000 inches on the real earth.

© Pilot Training Centre 1998

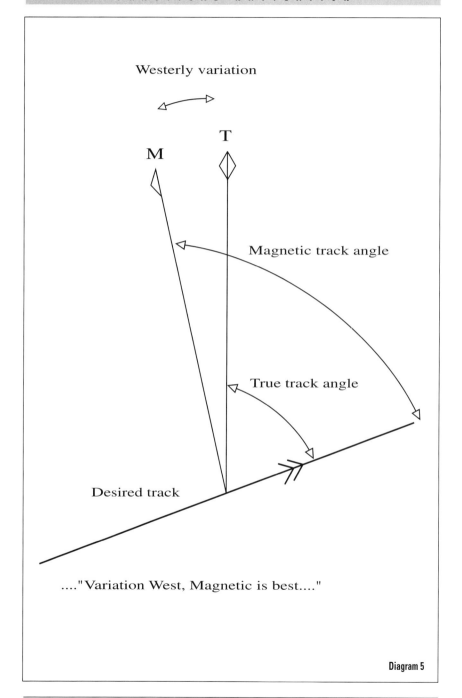

Westerly variation

T

M

Magnetic track angle

True track angle

Desired track

...."Variation West, Magnetic is best...."

Diagram 5

Hopefully you will agree that the distance is 44 nautical miles. Well, we have nearly finished the advance prep as I defined it earlier on in this session; there exists the need for a little further discussion on what altitude to fly at, what is a SAFE altitude to fly at and the selection of frequencies that you will use en route to talk to the various radar units.

When you decide on an altitude to fly at in the advanced prep stage, you must realise that you are only really looking for a band of altitudes within which you could fly at this stage, since the meteorological conditions on the day might have major repercussions here. You might like the earlier suggestion of flying at 3,500 feet but the cloudbase on the day might only be 2,000 feet. Would this be safe?

In order to get a safe band of altitudes in which to fly, you would have to consider two areas - one is how low could you fly both safely and legally and the other is how high could you fly staying clear of all of the upper bits of airspace?

Let's take the first case and look at a minimum operating altitude. A reminder here of aviation law would not go amiss. The lowest that you can fly is no closer than 500 feet to any person, vessel, vehicle or structure and even then this rule pre-supposes that you are not flying over congested areas or large crowds. What you then need to do is to follow along your track on your chart and check out the spot heights and contours to see what level the ground is at above mean sea level (AMSL). Having found this then you can add 500 feet to this in order to get your lowest operating altitude concurrent with staying legal above the highest bits of terrain. (You can actually fly within 500 feet of the ground but I would suggest that you are very likely to come within 500 feet of any persons, vessels, vehicles or structures and thus become illegal.) Obviously, operating at this altitude would mean that you would have to climb or go around any towns or villages and that you would have to pay particular attention to any obstacles such as tall masts or cables on or near your route. (A hint here; one such tall mast exists just to the east of track at 1226 feet AMSL).

The chart is drawn with a simple colour system to depict the high ground, which you will notice if you follow your track line along. We do in fact cross a ridge of high ground before Greenham Common and we pass just along the eastern edge of another ridge north of the M4. The white areas on the chart show the lower lying ground below 500 feet AMSL and then the code system depicts the land becoming progressively darker as it rises. (See the chart legend).

In the above paragraph, we picked a LEGAL minimum to operate at by taking the terrain level and adding 500 feet. I am quite certain however, that many of you would still consider this to be too low because you are thinking, quite rightly, that the engine could fail at any time and therefore you should choose to be higher than this. I would humbly suggest that you strongly consider flying at least 1000 feet above the highest terrain along your route - on the Oxford trip this equates to 2000 feet AMSL, as the ground rises to 974 feet just to the west of track. Please do be aware that if you ever do operate at the minimum level of 500 feet above ground level (AGL) then although the chart shows accurate spot heights, the land owner can actually build a mast up to 300 feet AGL and he is not required to tell anybody. SO IT WILL NOT APPEAR ON YOUR CHART!! Message clear??

So having decided that we should really only fly the route not below 2000 feet and that 3500 feet (from earlier observation) was a very sensible altitude to take for the least radio work, we should now concentrate on a maximum altitude.

When we start the route from Kingsworthy, we are temporarily held down to 2000 feet due to the Southampton control area (CTA) but as soon as we clear this then the only thing that puts a ceiling on our altitude is the airways system, which is coloured light blue on the chart.

Airways are essentially 'motorways' in the sky and come under the heading of controlled airspace. Like motorways, each airway has its own designator - R41 passes through Southampton; G1 runs out westwards from London, crossing our track north of Newbury; A1 tracks north west bound from Didcot to name but a few. Each airway has a base which is expressed sometimes as an altitude and at other times as a flight level and so the base of each one that you cross will have to be checked to ensure that you do not inadvertently enter the airway (absolutely verboten!!). Most airways are high enough so as not to pose a threat to many light single engine aeroplanes but do check each one. R41 for example, has a base at only FL35 (3,500 feet on an altimeter setting of 1013) as it passes over the Isle of Wight.

▶ PROJECT

Follow the Oxford track and identify each airway conflicting with it. Ascertain what the base of each airway is.

Other 'problems' that could arise airspace-wise include Terminal Manoeuvring Areas (TMA) and CTA's, which have already been mentioned. Basically a TMA is a buffer, if you like, between the airways system and a control zone. London has a very large set of TMA's known as the LTMA ('L' for London) and you would very definitely need to check the base of these when you operate anywhere in the south east of the UK. A further project then is for you to trace out the LTMA and look at its base. It is only then that you begin to realise that although the chart looks incredibly cluttered in light blue controlled airspace, much of it is in fact fairly high and is therefore of no consequence to us as light aeroplane pilots.

The above projects about the base of airways and TMA's are probably best conducted with either an experienced PPL or an instructor. You should by now realise that the LTMA lies east of our track and will not affect us and the lowest airway base is G1 on our route at flight level 55.

To recap. We looked at a minimum altitude and decided that although we were essentially LEGAL at 500 feet AGL (974 plus 500 feet, giving 1474 feet) we were not really very happy here lest the engine should fail; so we elected to fly at a minimum of 2,000 feet, which gave us 1,000 feet clear of the ground. Furthermore, we noted that the airways hold us down to a maximum of flight level 55. We can thus fly sensibly anywhere between the two limits imposed and we also observed that at 3500 feet the work was very much reduced because we would fly over all of the airspace 'problems'. That is about as far as we can go at present in the pre-planning stage on altitude selection. We would now need a knowledge of the actual cloudbase on the day to pick the actual operating altitude. There is not much left to do now in what I call the pre planning stages, except to tidy up and add in the frequencies that will be required in flight. The definitive place to get the correct radio frequencies is in the UK AIP (Air Pilot) under the COM section. Most PPLs use some form of flight guide, the most popular of which is Pooleys. Overleaf are included sample pages from the Pooleys guide and COM section of the U.K. Air Pilot. Obviously if you are flying frequently (and assuming your chart is up to date!) then you will become very familiar with many of the more local frequencies and there is a frequency table along the western edge of your chart. Some people remove this and attach it to their knee boards as a handy reference whilst flying.

I have entered what I believe to be the relevant frequencies on the plog. A number of military units appear on my list; this is because the military provide an excellent radar service (this is the 'LARS' that you can see written on the chart and indeed on the plog. It stands for Lower Airspace Radar Service). Furthermore, I have added a civilian airfield (Thruxton) in case of an airborne diversion being required. Please discuss the choice of frequencies with your instructor, as he or she may have some further ideas of their own.

When we spoke earlier of altitudes to fly at, we carefully by-passed mention of a column on the plog headed 'MSA'. This is for a concept known as minimum safe altitude. An MSA is selected prior to flight lest you inadvertently fly into cloud as a basic PPL, or student, or you can no longer determine your aeroplanes flightpath. Obviously in this instance you run the extremely serious and potentially fatal risk of flying either into the ground or into perhaps a mast. A severe case of the so called 'cumulus grannitus'! A couple of years ago I remember the case of a new PPL flying on his own on his first trip post PPL training. As I recall, the weather that day was fit for card playing only, which was what the CFI and I did all day! However, at an airfield not terribly far away from us, the hero of the story was getting airborne

SAMPLE POOLEYS
FLIGHT GUIDE PAGE - OXFORD

EGTK

N5150·06 W00119·14	**OXFORD (Kidlington)**	270 ft AMSL

6 nm NNW of Oxford.　　　　**CPT 114·35 355 21. DTY 116·40 206 22·1**
　　　　　　　　　　　　　　　　　　BNN 113·75 288 29·3
c/s Oxford. APP 125·325. TWR/AFIS* 118·875. GND 121·95. Dep ATIS 121·75.
VDF 125·325 (O/R) Brize Radar 134·30.
DME 'OX' 117·70 (On A/D). NDB 'OX' 403·50 (On A/D).　　* Sat, Sun & P. Hols.

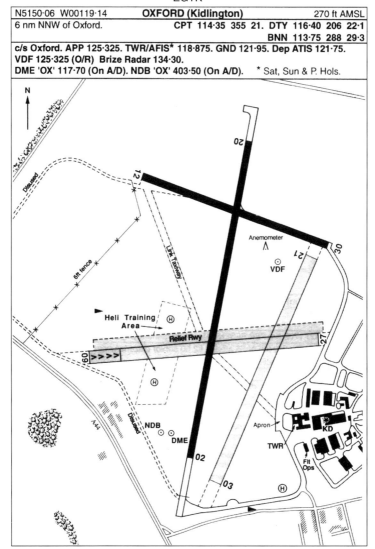

PAGE EXTRACT FROM
COM SECTION UK AIP (AIR PILOT)

Area	Service	Callsign	Emission	Frequency			Hours of Operation		Coordinates		Remarks
Solent Control / Solent Area	APP	Solent Approach	A3E	120.225	-	120.225	Mon-Fri 0625-2100 Sat 0625-2000 Sun 0735-2100 (and by arrangement)	Mon-Fri 0625-2000 Sat 0525-1900 Sun 0800-2000 (and by arrangement)	-	-	-
Southampton	APP	Southampton Approach	A3E	128.850 131.000	-	128.850 131.000	As directed by ATC	As directed by ATC	N5057.28 W00121.27	-	-
	TWR	Southampton Tower	A3E	118.200	-	118.200	As Solent CTA	As Solent CTA	N5057.27 W00121.25	-	-
	RAD	Southampton Radar	A3E	128.860	-	128.860	As directed by ATC	As directed by ATC	N5057.28 W00121.28	-	-
	ATIS	Southampton Information	A3E	113.350	-	-	HO	HO	N5056.49 W00121.59	-	Broadcast on Southampton VOR.
	LLZ / ILS RWY 20	ISN	A9W	110.750	-	-			N5057.28 W00121.27	-	On AD. DME Ch 44Y. ILS freq paired. Zero range is indicated at THR RWY 20 only. Aerial Hgt 45.92 ft amsl.
	GP	ISN		333.050	-	-				204	178 m from THR 20. 3.1° ILS Ref Datum Hgt 51 ft.
	DME	ISN	PON	1131	-	1068				-	On AD. DOC 100 nm/50000 ft Sector 225° to 315° MAG).
	L		NON A2A	391.5	-	-				-	On AD. Range 15 nm.
Southampton	Fire	Southampton Fire	A3E	121.600	-	121.600	Available when fire vehicle attending aircraft on the ground in emergency.		N5057.28 W00120.61	-	BAA Plc
	VOR	SAM	A9W	113.350	-	-	H24	H24	N5057.28 W00120.61	-	NATS Ltd. Approach Aid to Southampton DOC 100 nm/50000 ft (150 nm/50000 ft in Sector 225° to 315° MAG). DME Ch 80Y. Aerial Hgt 66 ft amsl.
	DME		PON	-	-	-				-	BAA Plc

...... Shortly after departure, the hapless PPL entered some very low cloud and spent a short while on instruments trying to descend out of the cloud until he felt an impact on the airframe whereupon he gave up, temporarily, trying to descend. A few minutes later this fellow did indeed become clear of cloud and managed to find his way back to his field of departure. During the landing his aircraft came to rest on its nose and propeller and was wrecked. The nosewheel and leg had been left on an unknown hillside during an impact with terra firma and fortunately for our subject, the aeroplane had bounced back into the air!

The mistakes made, apart from getting airborne in foul weather in the first place, included descending below a minimum safe altitude when the pilot encountered the cloud. The correct procedure would have been to have transferred to instruments, climbed to and levelled off at a safe altitude and declared an emergency.

So what is MSA? Well, basically it is an altitude that you have pre-selected that guarantees you a certain clearance above both the terrain and tall objects situated on it. It is quite irrelevant if it is good weather and you can easily determine your flight path and hence you can fly BELOW your MSA, BUT AS SOON AS YOU BECOME LOST OR INADVERTENTLY ENTER CLOUD YOU MUST IMMEDIATELY CLIMB TO AT LEAST YOUR SAFETY ALTITUDE. There are no hard and fast rules about how you work out an MSA. I take the tallest object or spot height within ten miles of my track and to this figure I add 1000 feet; I then round my result UP to the nearest 100 feet ABOVE this figure. Please note that 'within ten miles of track' also includes the ten miles before your start point and ten miles beyond your destination.

So MSA selection requires a fairly in depth study of your chart and route to find the highest areas; this is what I am advocating that you do anyway, as good flight planning pre-empts a good trip. Or as the RAF say, "Prior Planning Prevents P*** Poor Performance"! There is a faster way of obtaining a good safety altitude and that is to use the MEFs or Maximum Elevation Figures. These are the large blue figures printed in each quadrangle formed by the meridians of longitude (the north-south grid lines) and the parallels of latitude (the east-west lines). The MEF itself is not a safety altitude but the highest known object or contour in that area. It would be worth repeating that. THE MEF ITSELF IS NOT A SAFETY ALTITUDE BUT THE HIGHEST KNOWN OBJECT OR CONTOUR IN THAT AREA. To use the MEF for an MSA simply take the biggest MEF from each quadrangle that you pass through and add whatever factor you wish to have as a safety margin on top. As I have already said, I use 1,000 feet.

To give an example, our trip to Oxford passes just to the west of a mast at Kingsclere (find it!) which is 1,226´ AMSL or 498´ AGL. This is indeed the highest feature en route and the long handed way of calculating MSA would be to add 1000 feet and round up, giving 2300 feet. (Check it). Alternatively, follow up the track line taking the highest MEF. This is clearly marked as 1,300 feet. Adding 1,000 feet to this gives again 2,300 feet. So mark 2,300 on your plog under the column marked MSA. Incidentally, it is always useful to mark on your plog the point on which you based your MSA. In this case I have written it above the words MSA on the plog. This is so that somebody else looking at your plan can see whether or not you have missed something even higher. Incidentally, if you calculate the MSA using the MEF's then the extra 300′ for masts not already shown on the chart will have been taken into account. If you calculate an MSA the long handed way then if the highest item along your track was a spot height then you would need to add in a further 300′ to allow for the possibility of unmarked masts being present. (In other words the chart will not show masts that are less than 300 feet high.)

The last job to do in our advanced planning stage is to write on the plan which altimeter setting regions that we intend to fly through. You know the symbol for an ASR from one of your first projects so follow up your track line and see whether or not it crosses any ASR symbols. Where it does, simply take note of the name of the new region and enter this in the relevant box. You should find two regions in this way, including the one in which Southampton lies.

What is an ASR? An ASR is one of a number of named regions on your chart where the local sea level equivalent pressure (QNH) is calculated by met observers at many different places across that region. These QNH's are sent to the met office at Bracknell where they are collated; the lowest of all of the observed QNH's is then taken and this is then disseminated to all of the aviation fraternity as being that regions QNH. It is known as the 'regional QNH'. The advantages are thus :- Everyone flying within a particular region will all fly on one QNH unless they happen to be within a short distance of a particular aerodrome, in which case they will set that aerodromes actual QNH. So if two pilots in the same region set their altimeters to the same setting then despite any local variations in pressure, each pilot will know where the other one is with respect to their altitude. In other words 2,000′ will be 2,000′ on each altimeter. If that is unclear to you then go no further in flying until you understand altimetry. The reason that the lowest QNH is chosen as the regional QNH is for safety purposes and is the great advantage to this system. If you happen to be flying at the point where the lowest QNH was recorded then your altimeter would read correctly. If on the other hand you are flying elsewhere so that the pressure is higher then this would mean that your indicated altitude is actually lower than your actual altitude. In other words it is a safe way to operate.

The regional QNH is valid for one hour and it will not change within that hour. Furthermore, it is forecast an hour ahead of when it is in use so the upshot of all this is that you can get airborne with knowledge of the current QNH and the QNH that will be in use during the next hour. Handy if you fly an aeroplane without a radio.

Hopefully you will have found that the two regions of operation on this trip (the ASR's) are PORTLAND and COTSWOLD. These should be entered on your plog now.

So, the advanced prep is now complete and if we were actually flying this trip to Oxford then we would need to book an aeroplane from the flying club and ensure that we were in and waiting to fly a couple of hours prior to our slot. Eagle eyed readers will have noticed that above the distance box on the plog I have included the words 'On course:-' and that in the fuel planning block I have put in an average fuel burn figure of 7 gallons per hour (GPH).

ASCO VFR FLIGHT LOG

WEATHER	W/V	TEMP	IAS	TAS
2000'		90		
5000'		90		

CHX OFF	T/O	LAND	CHX ON

CALL SIGN	G-OPTC
PILOT	SMITH

AREA		
PORTLAND	QNH	
COTSWOLD	QNH	

FIELD		DEPARTURE	ARRIVAL
R/W			
QFE			
QNH			
WIND			
W X			

1226' MAST @ Kingsclere

On Course:

REV

FROM	TO	MSA	Alt	Trk (t)	Drift	Hdg (t)	Var	Hdg (m)	Dev'	Hdg (c)	G/S	Dist	Time	ETA	ETA	ATA
KINGSWORTHY	OXFORD	2300		359			4°W					44				

FACILITY	FREQ
BOSCOMBE DOWN	126.7 LARS
FARNBOROUGH	125.25 LARS
SOUTHAMPTON	118.2 tower
SOLENT	120.225
BENSON	120.9 LARS
BRIZE	134.3 LARS
OXFORD	125.325 ATC
	118.875 AFIS
THRUXTON	130.45

EMERGENCY	121.5
RADIO FAIL	7600
MAYDAY	7700

IMP GALLONS	
AVGE USE	7 gph
TAXI T/O	
TRIP	
APP LDG	
RESERVE	
MIN.REQ	
TOTAL FUEL ON	
MAX. ENDURANCE	

OBSERVATION

22

© Pilot Training Centre 1998

ON THE DAY PREPARATION

The first job on the day of your flight, apart from ensuring that the instructor is liberally anointed with tea to rehydrate him from the night before, is to collect the meteorological or met data. Personally I like to keep an eye on the BBC weather the night before ("Hurricane! What hurricane?" Michael Fish) and then peruse both the Lapforms 214 and 215 and the TAFs (Terminal Aerodrome Forecasts) to give me not only a reasonable picture of what is likely to occur but also what the spot winds and temperatures are forecast to be. (Then I collar somebody in flight planning who actually looks as though he knows what he is about and I casually ask him what he thinks of the weather - he is bound to have a better idea of what it all means than me! The trick is to appear to be only half listening, nod sagely at the right points but in reality listen like a hawk! QFI's are cunning like that!).

I have included a met-set here so that we can extract a sensible wind and temperature aloft for our flight and make some decisions about what altitude we are actually going to fly at. Obviously here is not the time and place to do a thorough study of these papers. However it is worth having a quick look at the documentation, as weather forecasting is a prominent part of the decision making process when it comes to a 'go/no go' debate. The weather chosen here was the weather as forecast on the 18th of August 1994. This particular day was selected because it was of interest with regard to a go/no go decision and maybe it might show you how practical flying decisions are made.

Basically the Lapform 215 (overleaf) shows an approaching polar front depression moving eastbound at 25 knots - a bog standard frontal system and a met book classic. The sort that gives forecasters paroxysms of delight; even I could predict what was going to happen! At 0900Z ('Z' for 'zulu' or UTC) the approaching warm front was way over to the west. Over Ireland in fact. This front, from the outlook picture, was scheduled to hit Southampton and Oxford at or around 1800Z. The dangers of flying near approaching warm fronts are well documented and include a lowering of the cloudbase, heavy rain, poor visibility and possibly rain ice ahead of and beneath the front. All in all not very nice! The problem arises when you look at the forecast and try to predict when all of the nastiness will occur. Generally the weather associated with a warm front deteriorates gradually as the front approaches you and the rain usually occurs about 150 to 200 miles ahead of the ground position of the front.

At 0900 hrs local time the weather was stunning! ('Eye-balling' the weather is another aspect of forecasting that experience will bring to you, though all too often this is ignored by many). On the forecast sheet this was borne out with the prediction for Zone 3 (the weather is split into zones of main interest) of 30 km visibility, nil weather and the possibility of up to 3 oktas (or eighths) of the sky

LAPFORM 215 WEATHER PROGNOSIS

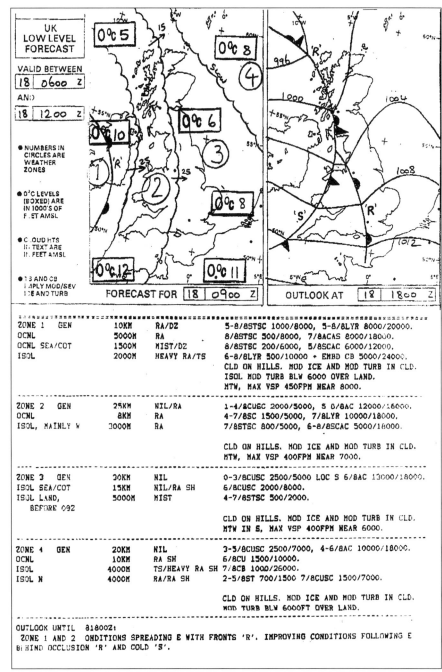

```
ZONE 1   GEN        10KM    RA/DZ           5-8/8STSC 1000/8000, 5-8/8LYR 8000/20000.
OCNL                5000M   RA              8/8STSC 500/8000, 7/8ACAS 8000/18000.
OCNL SEA/COT        1500M   MIST/DZ         8/8STSC 200/6000, 5/8SCAC 6000/12000.
ISOL                2000M   HEAVY RA/TS     6-8/8LYR 500/10000 + EMBD CB 5000/24000.
                                            CLD ON HILLS. MOD ICE AND MOD TURB IN CLD.
                                            ISOL MOD TURB BLW 6000 OVER LAND.
                                            MTW, MAX VSP 450FPM NEAR 8000.

ZONE 2   GEN        25KM    NIL/RA          1-4/8CUSC 2000/5000, 5 8/8AC 12000/16000.
OCNL                8KM     RA              4-7/8SC 1500/5000, 7/8LYR 10000/18000.
ISOL, MAINLY W      3000M   RA              7/8STSC 800/5000, 6-8/8SCAC 5000/18000.

                                            CLD ON HILLS. MOD ICE AND MOD TURB IN CLD.
                                            MTW, MAX VSP 400FPM NEAR 7000.

ZONE 3   GEN        30KM    NIL             0-3/8CUSC 2500/5000 LOC S 6/8AC 13000/18000.
ISOL SEA/COT        15KM    NIL/RA SH       6/8CUSC 2000/8000.
ISOL LAND,          5000M   MIST            4-7/8STSC 500/2000.
   BEFORE 092
                                            CLD ON HILLS. MOD ICE AND MOD TURB IN CLD.
                                            MTW IN S, MAX VSP 400FPM NEAR 6000.

ZONE 4   GEN        20KM    NIL             3-5/8CUSC 2500/7000, 4-6/8AC 10000/18000.
OCNL                10KM    RA SH           6/8CU 1500/10000.
ISOL                4000M   TS/HEAVY RA SH  7/8CB 1000/26000.
ISOL N              4000M   RA/RA SH        2-5/8ST 700/1500 7/8CUSC 1500/7000.

                                            CLD ON HILLS. MOD ICE AND MOD TURB IN CLD.
                                            MOD TURB BLW 6000FT OVER LAND.

OUTLOOK UNTIL  81800Z:
   ZONE 1 AND 2  ONDITIONS SPREADING E WITH FRONTS 'R'. IMPROVING CONDITIONS FOLLOWING E
B: HIND OCCLUSION 'R' AND COLD 'S'.
```

covered by cumulus or strato-cumulus. The south could also expect some very much higher alto-cumulus between 13,000 and 18,000 feet. Zone 2, which would shortly be on us, warned of a general dropping of the cloud base and a worsening of the visibility until eventually we would see only 3,000m in rain with a cloudbase of 800 feet. It concludes with the rather ominous warning of cloud ON the hills and ice/turbulence in the cloud. Mountain wave is also predicted. Heavens above! The only good sign is that the rain is well to the west.

The ground position of the front makes up Zone 1's weather and does not make good reading! There again, anything mentioning 1,500 metres visibility and 8 oktas of stratus and stratocumulus between 200 and 6,000 feet rarely does! (And I didn't even mention the heavy rain, thunderstorms, embedded cumulo-nimbus and turbulence associated with this zone!).

My thoughts on the weather are therefore thus:- the weather IS good enough to contemplate our route; with the proviso that it is flown dual (i.e. with an experienced instructor) and soon so that the aircraft is either returning promptly or will be remaining overnight to sit the weather out. The weather definitely is NOT suitable to contemplate any solo work other than that which is conducted close to the home base under close supervision; this is due to the anticipated deterioration in the weather. As I said previously, an interesting go/no go decision.

The second met sheet shown overleaf is known as the Lapform 214 and it shows both the spot winds and temperatures at various levels. The data is contained in boxes and is valid for a given grid reference, expressed in latitude and longitude. We haven't touched very much on this system of position marking except when we mentioned the meridians as defining the true north-south directions. Before I talk about the 214 then, I can see that I am about to digress a little and BRIEFLY explain something about lat. and long.

Taking the meridians, which are actually called meridians of longitude, we have a special case meridian called the Greenwich Meridian or the "Prime Meridian". The Greenwich Meridian is a circle on the earths' surface running from pole to pole through Greenwich. (From previous study you will be familiar with the concept that this meridian therefore defines the direction of true north locally at Greenwich). If you took a line inwards from the Greenwich Meridian to the centre of the earth and then another line from the centre of the earth back out towards your feet then the angle between the two lines would be the angle of **LONGITUDE**. This would obviously lie to the east or west of the Greenwich Meridian. Longitude is always expressed as a three digit group of figures as you could go a maximum of 180 degrees either to the west or to the east. If I were to go 181 degrees to the east then clearly it would be faster going 179 degrees to the west! The convention therefore, is always to use the shorter angular distance.

LAPFORM 214 WIND & TEMPERATURE CHART

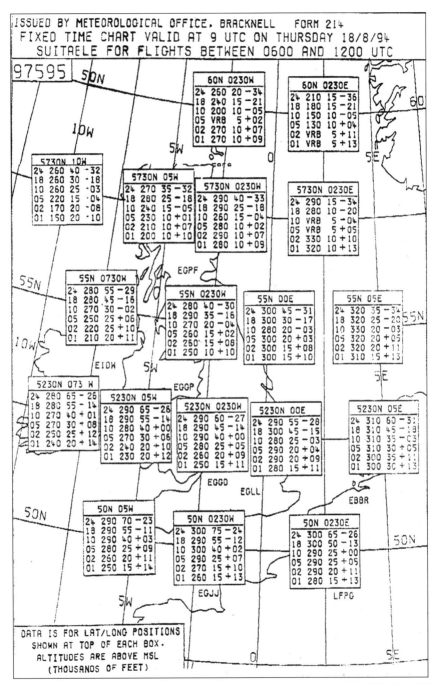

ISSUED BY METEOROLOGICAL OFFICE, BRACKNELL   FORM 214
FIXED TIME CHART VALID AT 9 UTC ON THURSDAY 18/8/94
SUITABLE FOR FLIGHTS BETWEEN 0600 AND 1200 UTC

97595 50N

10W

5W

60N 0230W
24 260 20 -34
18 240 15 -21
10 200 10 -05
05 VRB 5 +02
02 270 10 +07
01 270 10 +09

60N 0230E
24 210 15 -36
18 180 15 -21
10 150 10 -05
05 130 10 +04
02 VRB 5 +11
01 VRB 5 +13

60

5E

0

5730N 10W
24 260 40 -32
18 260 30 -18
10 260 25 -03
05 220 15 -04
02 170 20 -08
01 150 20 -10

5730N 05W
24 270 35 -32
18 280 25 -18
10 240 15 -05
05 230 10 +01
02 210 10 +07
01 200 10 +10

5730N 0230W
24 290 40 -33
18 290 25 -18
10 260 15 -04
05 280 10 +02
02 290 10 +07
01 280 10 +09

5730N 0230E
24 290 15 -34
18 280 10 -20
10 VRB 5 -04
05 VRB 5 +05
02 330 10 +10
01 320 10 +13

EGPF

5SN 0730W
24 280 55 -29
18 280 45 -16
10 270 30 -02
05 250 25 +06
02 220 25 +10
01 210 20 +11

5SN 0230W
24 280 40 -30
18 290 35 -16
10 270 20 -04
05 260 15 +02
02 250 15 +08
01 250 10 +10

5SN 00E
24 300 45 -31
18 300 30 -17
10 280 20 -03
05 300 20 +03
02 300 15 +08
01 300 15 +10

5SN 05E
24 320 35 -34
18 320 25 -20
10 330 20 -03
05 320 20 +05
02 320 20 +11
01 310 15 +13

55N

EIDW

5W

5E

5230N 073 W
24 280 65 -26
18 280 55 -14
10 270 40 +01
05 270 30 +08
02 250 25 +12
01 240 20 +14

5230N 05W
24 290 65 -26
18 290 55 -14
10 280 40 +00
05 270 30 +06
02 240 20 +10
01 230 20 +11

5230N 0230W
24 290 60 -27
18 290 45 -14
10 290 40 +00
05 280 25 +05
02 260 20 +09
01 250 15 +11

5230N 00E
24 290 55 -28
18 300 45 -15
10 280 25 -03
05 290 20 +04
02 290 20 +09
01 280 15 +11

5230N 05E
24 310 60 -31
18 310 45 -18
10 310 35 -05
05 310 30 +05
02 300 35 +11
01 300 30 +13

EGGP

EGGO

EGLL

EBBR

50N

50N 05W
24 290 70 -23
18 290 55 -11
10 290 40 +03
05 280 25 +09
02 260 20 +11
01 250 15 +14

50N 0230W
24 300 75 -24
18 290 55 -12
10 300 40 +02
05 290 25 +07
02 270 15 +10
01 260 15 +13

50N 0230E
24 300 65 -26
18 300 50 -13
10 290 25 +00
05 290 25 +05
02 290 20 +11
01 280 15 +13

50N

EGJJ

LFPG

DATA IS FOR LAT/LONG POSITIONS
SHOWN AT TOP OF EACH BOX.
ALTITUDES ARE ABOVE MSL
(THOUSANDS OF FEET)

Now if I measured myself as being stood on the 5 degree west line of longitude then this actually only defines another meridian i.e. a line running from pole to pole. I wouldn't actually know where I were along this line and so I need to employ a further system so as to pinpoint my position on the earths' surface. This is where we bring in the subject of latitude.

The starting point for latitude is the equator. We have already described a situation where we are stood on the 5 degree west meridian and wish to tie down our exact location along this meridian. Imagine the point at which this meridian and the equator intersect. Insert a line mentally from this point inwards to the centre of the earth and then another line running outwards again to your feet. The angle between these two lines is called the angle of latitude. If this angle lies above the equator then you have a northerly latitude and if it lies below the equator then you have a southerly latitude.

Tie both a latitude and a longitude together and you have a position! It can't be a bad system - its been in use since God was in short trousers! A picture is worth a thousand words and so I have drawn you diagrams 6-8 overleaf but remember, a globe is worth many more! Recap on my words, look at the drawing but grab a globe! It really is much easier trying to visualise 'lat. and long' in this way.

Having digressed (for a reason) let us come back to the Lapform 214. This is essentially an outline of the U.K. with various boxes containing the important data required for some very sneaky navigation calculations - the winds and temperatures aloft. Each box contains the relevant met data for a given latitude and longitude shown at the top of the box. If you consult both the 214 and your navigation chart then you will see that if the wind/temp data were averaged between the boxes marked '50N 0230W' and '5230N 00E' then you would have a reasonable approximation to the average wind across our track.

From our earlier studies of the 215, we know that the weather will 'go down' soon but eyeball observations (and indeed the Southampton 'actual') show the cloudbase to be very high at present. This is useful because at this moment in time we can plan to fly the route at 3,500 feet where it has already been noted that the r/t workload should be a lot lighter. Therefore, taking the data box for 50N 0230W and extrapolating between the 2,000 and 5,000 feet information, we can see that the 3,500 feet wind should be 280/20. That is to say that the wind direction has been averaged between the 2,000 foot direction of 270 degrees and the 5,000 foot direction of 290 degrees. Since the 2,000 foot speed was 15 knots and the 5,000 foot speed was forecast to be 25 then averaging them gives 20 knots. Remember that winds *blow from* the direction given; we do not want any 'sucking' winds arriving here! Following the same sort of averaging process for the 5230N 00E box gives the 3,500 foot wind here as being 290/20. Now these winds that we have just

ANGLE OF LONGITUDE

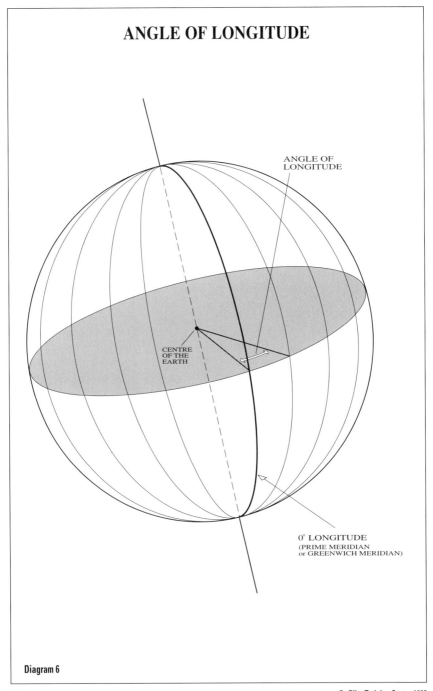

ANGLE OF
LONGITUDE

CENTRE
OF THE
EARTH

0° LONGITUDE
(PRIME MERIDIAN
or GREENWICH MERIDIAN)

Diagram 6

ANGLE OF LATITUDE

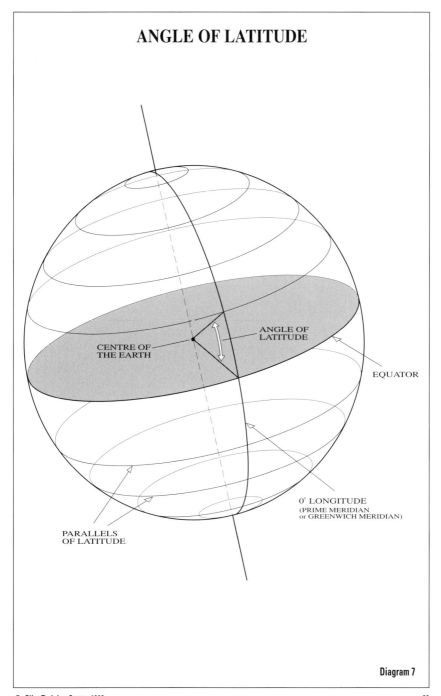

Diagram 7

LATITUDE & LONGITUDE GRID

THE EARTH
AS A SPHERE

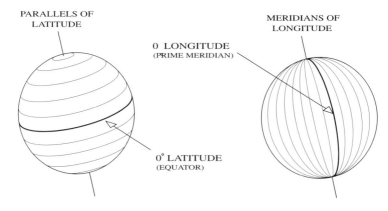

PARALLELS OF
LATITUDE

MERIDIANS OF
LONGITUDE

0 LONGITUDE
(PRIME MERIDIAN)

0° LATITUDE
(EQUATOR)

A LATTICE GRID OF
LINES OF LATITUDE
AND LONGITUDE

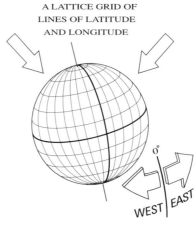

0°

WEST EAST

Diagram 8

determined must again be averaged because our track lies somewhere close to the mid-point between these 'spot winds'. So the average between 280/20 and 290/20 is 285/20. This 3,500 foot wind should now be marked in the meteorological data box at the top left hand corner of the plog.

Also from the 214 we can extract the temperature at our required level of 3,500 feet, again going through the same method of first averaging between the respective 2,000 and 5,000 feet levels to get the 3,500´ temperature for the two boxes and then averaging between these to get the route 3,500´ temperature. The temperature incidentally, is the last column of figures in each box. If you follow this procedure then you should find that the route temperature at 3,500´ becomes 7 and 1/2 degrees celsius, which I have called 7 degrees because when we use this shortly in our airspeed calculation you will realise that even whole numbers of degrees are difficult to set on your hand held navigation computer (whizzwheel).

Mark the temperature on your plog next to the 3,500´ wind. You may recall that earlier I had you mark 90 in the IAS or Indicated Airspeed column because this was the speed that we were going to fly the AA5 at. Well, yes the Grumman will be flown to read this on the airspeed indicator but in reality the aircraft is flying at a different speed known as your true airspeed or TAS. We obviously need to know the true or real speed of the flying machine in order that we can accurately navigate.

An airspeed indicator or ASI works by measuring the dynamic pressure of the air as you fly. Air is taken via the pitot tube in order to do this. Without delving too deeply into how the instrument works at this point, you should be aware that the pitot air enters a capsule which can expand or contract depending on the pressure of the air both inside of and surrounding the capsule. The capsules' movement can thus be related to how fast the aeroplane is moving because this will vary the pressure of the air entering via the pitot tube. So all we have to do is use what in the RAF vernacular is termed a 'SSOGAL' to connect the capsule to the needle of your airspeed indicator. (SSOGAL, it transpires, is a 'suitable system of gears and levers'! Acronyms gone mad!).

The ASI is thus calibrated according to the international standard atmosphere (ISA) of which you will learn much about during met lectures. Basically ISA is an 'average' atmosphere used throughout the world for calibration purposes. It is described in terms of the sea level conditions of temperature, pressure and density and how these values change with an increase of altitude. So if the conditions in which you are flying resemble ISA then you have a correctly reading ASI and everything is hunky-dory! However, the odds of actually experiencing ISA conditions are long indeed and so we must accustom ourselves to the idea that our ASI is reading incorrectly. It is the density of the air entering our pitot tube which is important and the factor having the most significant effect on this is the air temperature at the level at which we are flying. Hence the careful noting of this on the 214. Another piece of the puzzle falls into place!

ISA by the way, has a sea level temperature of +15°C and a lapse rate of 1.98°C per 1000′ climbed. The temperature decreases uniformly to -56.5°C at 36,090′ whereupon it is assumed to be constant at this for every altitude. The sea level density is 1225 gms/m cubed. Learn these figures and you will pass questions on at least three of your PPL examinations!

Imagine flying on a day where the air is warmer than that predicted under ISA. The warmer air is less dense than normal and so as you continue to fly, this air will have less 'push' in it when it enters the capsule of the ASI. In other words, the capsule will not expand so much and as a result the ASI will not show as fast an airspeed as it would have done on a standard day, even though the aeroplane is doing the same speed. That is to say that the indicated airspeed is less than the true airspeed. The opposite is true on a colder than standard day.

Grab your 'whizzwheel' and let's have a look at the effect that the air temperature has on the speed indications at 3,500 for our trip. What you have to do is look at the computer on the calculator side - that's the complicated looking side that is reminiscent of a slide rule. This is because that is exactly what it is - a circular slide rule. There are a couple of cut-out 'windows' on this side and we will be using the one marked 'Airspeed'. Two scales are visible in the window - one is altitude and the other is temperature. Moving the circular face of the computer it becomes obvious that you can set a particular combination of altitude and temperature together, although you must take care when doing this because the temperature scale is unconventional in that '+' values lie to the left of zero and '-' to the right. So set the forecast values together on your computer and to recap these are 3,500′ and +7°c. Make sure now that having set your machine up, you do not move it until I have described how to extract the TAS from it.

A little theory first. When you fly, your airspeed indicator, or ASI, reads indicated airspeed (IAS). Like any instrument, it is prone to instrument error, although this is not likely to be at all significant; probably of the order of less than a knot or so. Generally therefore, we ignore this error. Had we taken it into account then the IAS would have been corrected or rectified, giving us what is known as rectified airspeed or RAS. The Americans call this calibrated airspeed or CAS. Since we are going to ignore instrument error (do please confirm that in your aeroplane this is a small quantity before becoming ignorant of it. This can be checked in the pilots' operating handbook) then our IAS is in fact also our RAS. Look again at your whizzwheel. On the outermost edge of the calculator you should have two scales, one bearing the mark 'RAS' and the other displaying 'TAS'. To find out what your TAS is, you merely go to the RAS scale and at your appropriate IAS you read up to

THE AIRSPEED CALCULATION

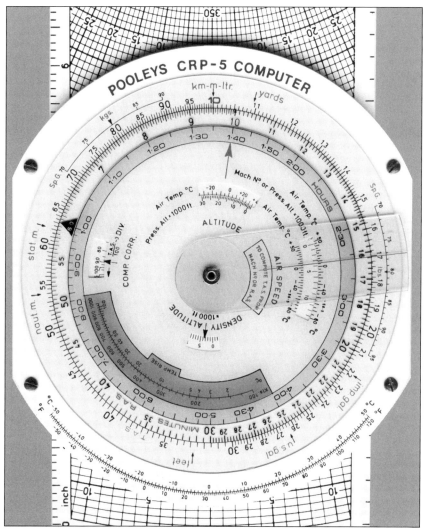

Diagram 9

the TAS scale and see what number is adjacent to your IAS. This is your TAS.

Since the calculator is already set up then go to your IAS of 90kt (from the plog, remember?) and read up to the TAS scale. You should see that 95kt is the displayed TAS. Enter this on your plog in the top left hand box.

When you fly, remember that you are going to set the throttle and use 'Power; Attitude; Trim' to give you an IAS of 90kt, the same as you have always done. It is just that now you happen to have the explicit knowledge that if the temperature were really as forecast then you will actually be travelling at a true airspeed of 95kt. In other words you fly at 90 but navigate at 95. You therefore go into the remaining navigation calculations using 95 but fly apparently at 90.

Turn your computer over now to the relatively uncomplicated and uncluttered navigation side and put it down while I brief you on how to find out what heading we are going to fly on and at what the groundspeed is.

The wind at 3,500 feet, if you cast your minds back, was 285/20. In other words the wind is blowing from a direction of 285° measured with respect to true north at a speed of 20kt. Our intended track is 359°, also relative to true north. Now if we are to fly approximately north with a westerly wind and we point the nose of the aeroplane approximately northwards towards our target then we will be blown off track and to the right. We will in fact miss our destination because we have not allowed for the effect of the wind. This might seem blindingly obvious to you and I hope that it does but it is the basis of our navigation calculation.

Grab your whizzwheel again! Firstly the wind must be entered into it. Move the rotating bezel (that's the moving ring to you, guv!) around so that the wind direction of 285° in this case is displayed at the top, which is known as the heading index. In the centre of your computer there is a circle with a dot inside of it. I call this dot the "TAS dot". If you have a computer with a squared off section at the bottom then move the TAS dot down to the top of this portion. If you do not have this square segment on your machine do not panic. Merely put your TAS dot on any convenient arced line, preferably on a whole number of tens. What you must do now is to mark a cross with a pencil below the TAS dot by 20kt. (Each tiny square represents 2kt). Finally, move the TAS dot up so that is resting on the arced line delineating 95; i.e. enter your TAS.

What you should have now is a computer displaying a heading into wind of 285° and a TAS of 95kt. The cross that you have drawn in is called the 'wind-cross' and it should be lying on the 75kt arc. It represents your speed over the ground (groundspeed) and so quite logically if you head into wind at 95 then you will cover the ground at 75.

ENTERING THE WIND

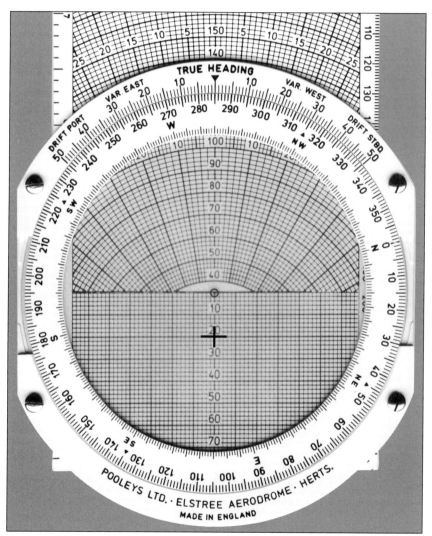

Diagram 10

...AND SETTING THE TAS OF 95°

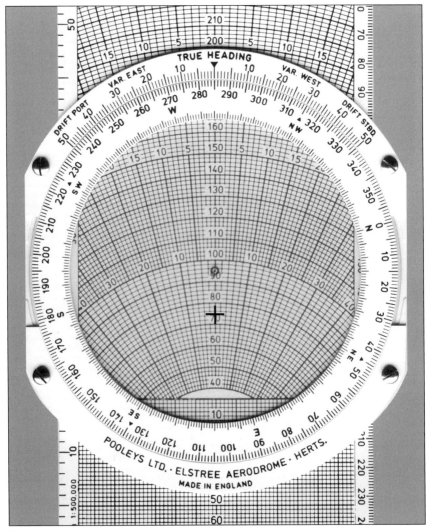

Diagram 11

Having entered the wind, I now want you to temporarily deny all knowledge of it (this should come easily to most students!!) and to point the nose of the aeroplane straight at your destination. In other words, rotate the bezel until 359° is under the heading index. We already know that the aeroplane will be blown off of our track to the right if we did this. Look at the computer and the wind cross. The wind cross should now be lying some 12° to the right as indicated by the straight drift lines. (See diagram 12). What this is telling you is that if you ignore the wind and head in the same direction as your intended track then you will err by 12° to the right. Very good, but you missed your target and bombed the wrong side!!

Let's take a second bite at the cherry. If you know that in making your heading the same as your track direction you missed by 12° to the right then why not simply head off 12° to the left, or 347°? Sounds good to me. You do not even have to do the sum of 359-12 = 347 because you can use the Martyn Smith 'patent' computer method here which does it for you! Simply hold the computer in both of your hands with each thumb on their respective sides of the bezel ring. You can see that the wind cross lies 12° right so move your right thumb down until the figure displayed under the heading index has changed by 12°. Vice versa had the cross been to the left. Lo and behold, the computer is now showing 347° under the heading index without you having to do a single sum and therefore there should be no likelihood of you getting it wrong. (See diagram 13).

There is of course one potential snag with this method and it is this. When we initially headed 359°, the wind made an angle of 74° with the longitudinal axis of the aircraft (359-285) and gave us a drift of 12°. When we turn to the left by 12° we are still expecting to get a drift of 12° so that we drift along our track. However, the wind now makes an angle of 62° with the aeroplane and it may mean that the drift changes from the hoped-for 12°. If this happens then there is a further bit of jiggery-pokery that we can do, but more of this later should this occur. If it does not arise then I will find you an example where it does in an appendix. (Appendix 2).

Right, let's get down to it. Turn the ring to the right until there is a change of 12° under the heading index, confirming that you are now indicating a heading of 347°. Now re-read your drift. Is it still 12°? Hopefully you are in agreement with me that the drift remains on 12°. This then is your true heading to fly because the navigators' crosscheck confirms that 347° plus 12° right drift does indeed give a track over the ground of 359°, which we are trying to achieve. Always do this mental cross check as it often is the only way of detecting any errors that you make at this point.

Now you have finished moving the whizzwheel, read off which arc that the wind cross centre lies on because this is your groundspeed. Confirm that you have this as 88 kt and then mark in both this and the heading under their relevant columns on the plog.

POINTING THE AEROPLANE AT YOUR DESTINATION (359°)

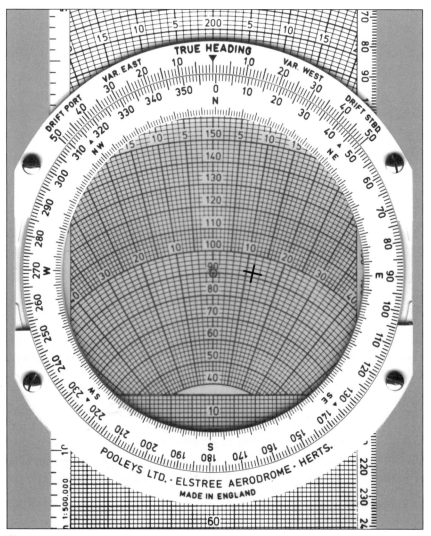

Diagram 12

ALLOWING FOR THE DRIFT OF 12°

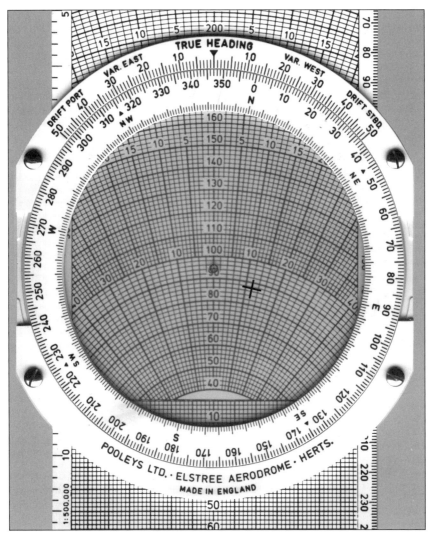

Diagram 13

Easy really, wasn't it? Buy my book called 'Diversion Planning' and it will show you how to do all of that in your head with almost the same accuracy! That's a little more advanced though, for the moment.

Once you have marked in the heading then the variation which was previously noted as 4°W can be utilised. Remember the rhyme that stated "Variation west, Magnetic is best"? Well, this means that the magnetic heading must be some 4° bigger than the true heading and so you can note the magnetic heading down on your plan as being 351°M.

Still ignoring the columns headed 'Dev' and 'Hdg C' until we are safely seated in a particular aeroplane we now consider the business of calculating the time of flight from Kingsworthy to Oxford. We have a groundspeed which is your TAS corrected for the effect of the wind to give you the actual speed that you are travelling over the earth and we have a ground distance that was measured from the chart (44 nm). The relationship between speed, distance and time is very straightforward.

Speed (V) = Distance (S) ÷ Time (T)

The groundspeed as ascertained by the computer was measured in knots (kt) or nautical miles per hour (ie 88 nm in 60 minutes). So the 88 kt groundspeed is equal to our 44 nm distance divided by an unknown or as yet to be worked out time. Mathematically, this would look like the following equation :-

88nm / 60 mins = 44nm / T

Setting this up on your whizzwheel couldn't be any simpler. Using the calculator side again, simply think of the quotient or dividing line (the horizontal line between the '88' and the '60' and between the '44' and 'T') as being the border between the two scales on the outer ring of your computer. All you do is set the black, triangular '60' marker on the inner scale adjacent to the groundspeed of '88' on the outer (see overleaf). You have now set the computer for any calculation using an 88kt groundspeed. Remembering in our original sum that speed is distance over time then it follows that the outer scale is distance and the inner is time. So find 44 nm on the outer scale and read the figure beneath this on the inner scale and lo and behold this is the time taken to fly 44 nm at 88 kt. No prizes to the 'smart' navigators here, who realised that 88nm in 60 minutes was obviously the same as

GROUNDSPEED / TIME CALCULATION

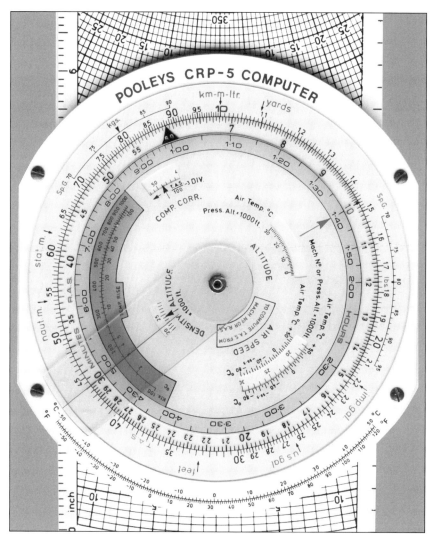

Diagram 14

44 nm in 30 minutes without using their calculators! Incidentally, had you got a groundspeed and wanted to know how far you could go in a set time then all you do is set up the groundspeed against 60 as before but then you read up from the number of minutes on the inner scale to the number displayed above this on the outer. This is the distance flown in that time.

Hopefully we are in agreement that our respective whizzwheels give a time of 30 minutes. Mark the time in on the relevant box on the plan (shown overleaf).

One of the final jobs to do in this section is the fuel planning. Do you remember way back in the text that I said that the AA5 was going to burn 7 gallons of fuel per hour? So a 30 minute journey should burn 3 and $^1/_2$ gallons, agreed? WRONG!!! You will need to allow a certain amount of fuel, say 2 gallons, for start up and taxiing. A further couple of gallons will be consumed in the take off and climb out en route to Kingsworthy. Also, a couple of gallons should be allowed for the circuit flown on arrival and the landing. In point of fact most of this bit is superfluous as it will be flown at fairly low power settings as you descend. However, as soon as fuel planning comes into play then I automatically start over-estimating my requirements grossly - working along the principle of "a couple of extra gallons for the wife and kids" is not a bad way of thinking. Obviously you may be in a position where you are unable to load up with lots of fuel - eg on a hot summers afternoon with a heavily laden aeroplane and a short runway but that is another story. Do bear in mind though, the old adage that "there's nothing so useless to you when you're flying than the fuel you left behind in the bowser"!! Finished your fuel plan yet? WRONG (again)!! What about the possibility of diverting either en route or from the overhead at Oxford? On a short trip like this you might like to carry perhaps an hours diversion fuel because there are lots of airfields about. You might consider carrying lots more in differing circumstances.........

The basic plan is now complete and our attention must now be turned to chart preparation and finding suitable points along track with which to fix our position. These practical considerations will be covered in the next section called 'Chart Prep' before, in the final part, we show you how to put all of this into operation in the air.

ASCO VFR FLIGHT LOG

WEATHER	W/V	TEMP	IAS	TAS
3500'	285/20	+7	90	95

CHX OFF	T/O	LAND	CHX ON

	CALL SIGN	G-OPTC
	PILOT	SMITH

	AREA	QNH	QNH
PORTLAND			
COTSWOLD			

	DEPARTURE	ARRIVAL
FIELD		
R/W		
QFE		
QNH		
WIND	W X	

1226' MAST @ Kingsclere

FROM	TO	MSA	Alt	Trk (t)	Drift	Hdg (t)	Var	Hdg (m)	Dev'	Hdg (c)	G/S	Dist	Time	ETA	ETA	ATA
KINGSWORTHY	OXFORD	2300	3500	359	12°s	347	4°W	351			88	44	30			

On Course: | REV |

FACILITY	FREQ
SOUTHAMPTON	118.2 tower
SOLENT	120.225
BOSCOMBE DOWN	126.7 LARS
FARNBOROUGH	125.25 LARS
BENSON	120.9 LARS
BRIZE	134.3 LARS
OXFORD	125.325 ATC
THRUXTON	118.875 AFIS
	130.45

EMERGENCY	121.5
RADIO FAIL	7600
MAYDAY	7700

IMP GALLONS	
AVGE USE	7 gph
TAXI T/O	2+2
TRIP	3½
APP LDG	2
RESERVE	7
MIN REQ	16½
TOTAL FUEL ON	30
MAX. ENDURANCE	4 hrs

OBSERVATION

Chart Preparation

So far, we are left with a plan and a chart containing only your track line. Since navigation is all about time then the first thing that has to be done is a little chart calibration if you like. By that I mean that we are going to put a 'ruler' of time on your chart. Confused?!! It's quite easy, really. The question you must ask yourself is how far are we going to travel in a fixed amount of time and then we shall divide the track up into those sized portions, thus giving a planned time scale. Now the fundamental unit for navigational time at these speeds is six minutes. Why? Well, since there are sixty minutes to an hour then six of them represent one tenth of that hour. So what's the big deal? Well, if you divide the groundspeed by ten (and that's so easy you can do it in your head) then you have the distance that you should travel, in 6 minutes, at your planned groundspeed. So at 88 kt, you would travel 8.8 nm. Therefore, if you start at the beginning of your track and mark up every 8.8 nm then you have a visual representation on the chart of your groundspeed. Take your ruler and mark off a line at every 8.8 nm. In point of fact you would 'guesstimate' the 8.8 as being halfway between 8.5 and 9, which you can see on the ruler.

Now we have calibrated the chart, it is possible to pick some fix features for use as we actually navigate, which is the subject of this section. A fix feature must be prominent and it must be unique. You must be certain that as you navigate you have correctly identified the relevant fix because you may have to change your plan in the air based upon where you find yourself with respect to a fix and that is why we are looking for uniqueness. If you mis-identify a fix and 'correct' your heading or your groundspeed then you run the risk of getting lost!

Another area to look at with fixes is the spacing in between them. It is pointless having an excellent fix partway up your route, only to use another one three minutes flying time further on. That would just be a waste of time. At the sort of speeds that we are currently considering then you might like to choose fix points no closer than say, six minutes apart and yet no more than about twelve minutes apart since you do not want to allow a navigational error too long in order to build up before you become aware of it.

Looking at our route, I have chosen three prominent fixes, which is ample for our requirements. The first is the Andover to Basingstoke railway line. The 'calibrated' chart shows that we should cross this line, funnily enough, exactly on the six minute mark! This is not intentional and I must point out here that we are not looking for features at the six minute marks; rather we are looking for an obvious feature and then seeing at what time we plan to cross it. Had the railway line turned up at 7 and ¼ minutes then so be it. Ordinarily, line features that cross track are only good for checking the groundspeed (i.e. that they are crossed at the correct time), however if you consult the chart then you will see that we plan to cross the line between

Whitchurch and Overton and these two towns make the feature unique enough for our use. The second fix is the southern edge of the town of Newbury. Amazingly this occurs at twelve minutes!! The third and final fix could have been Harwell, the town in the centre of the prohibited area P106 (a reminder here not to cross this below two and a half thousand feet), but I have decided to stretch it out for a further twelve minutes and to use the airfield at Abingdon since we should track right through its' overhead and it is very prominent. Would you believe that this occurs at twenty four minutes on the nose?!!

In the 'Observations' block on the plog I would like you to write down each selected fix and to mark alongside this the planned time of arrival at each, in terms of elapsed time.

The remaining chart job is the marking in of fan lines on one side of your track. Fan lines are lines offset from the beginning and end of your track by 10° so that they assist you in 'guesstimating' angles should you need to correct your heading in flight. Have a look at the prepared section of chart showing these lines.

The theory of the fan lines use is relatively straightforward (like all of the nav so far!). When you see your fix point, you must decide whether you are on track or not. If you determine that you are to one side or another of track then a heading correction is called for. If you mentally mark in a line from your start point to your present position then the angle between this line and your track line is called your track error. Now working on the assumption that because you have planned your flight reasonably well (it is hoped!) then your track error will not be too great. We make use of the fact that a small heading change will not significantly alter the drift and thus will produce the same change in your track made good over the ground. So if you have a track error of 8°, then turning through 8° will produce an 8° change of track. If this happens then you will parallel your original planned track and should not deviate from it any further. You are however, still displaced to one side of your planned track and further action will have to be taken in order to hit the target.

Since you are off track then your planned track is now superfluous to requirements as you will obviously want to fly the track from your actual position to the target. The angle between this new track and the old one is called the closing angle. Since we are already paralleling our old track then a little thought about parallel lines and angles (remember your geometry from school?!!) should show you that the closing angle is also the further amount that we would need to turn through, in order to follow the new required track and thus arrive at the destination.

Let us recap (See diagram 15). If you are off track :- (1) Assess your track error and (2) assess the closing angle. (3) Add these quantities together and turn by this total amount. Hopefully I shouldn't have to explain that if you are left of track then a right turn is needed..................?!!

LOST?

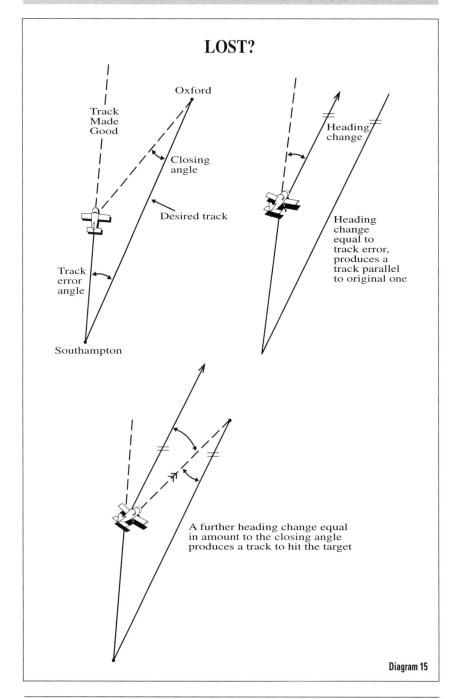

Oxford

Track Made Good

Closing angle

Desired track

Track error angle

Southampton

Heading change

Heading change equal to track error, produces a track parallel to original one

A further heading change equal in amount to the closing angle produces a track to hit the target

Diagram 15

46

Now all the fan lines do is give you a visual representation of what a 10° track error and closing angle look like at various distances. Get it? If you are good at assessing angles then leave them out as an unnecessary encumbrance.

Although we have a PLOG or plan compiled, some navigators like to transfer this to the chart and so, at a convenient point on each leg, they draw in a box with their heading and the leg time in it which is, after all, the only information immediately required. Also, some pilots like to highlight their fix points with a circle so that the track line does not obscure any ground detail when it is required. The planned fix time is also marked alongside each fix.

One last good idea is to mark in the forecast wind vector on your chart (a vector quantity is described in terms of a speed and a direction), remembering that winds blow from a given direction and not towards it! There are no 'sucking winds' in my book! If you have read my first book, 'Diversion Planning' (and why not; hundreds of others have already!), then you will realise just how useful this wind vector can be to you in the event of a diversion.

We are ready to play now! The next instalment shows you exactly how we are going to use this extensive plan to actually arrive at a destination, so pin back your lug holes and be ready to absorb............ (Overleaf is a prepared flight log; '351°C' is the compass heading, not the magnetic heading. The next section refers).

ASCO VFR FLIGHT LOG

WEATHER	W/V	TEMP	IAS	TAS
3500'	285/20	7	90	95

CHX OFF	T/O	LAND	CHX ON

CALL SIGN	G-OPTC
PILOT	SMITH

AREA	QNH	QNH
PORTLAND		
COTSWOLD		

	FIELD
	R/W
	QFE
	QNH
DEPARTURE	WIND
	W X

ARRIVAL

1226' MAST @ Kingsclere

FROM	TO	MSA	Alt	Trk (t)	Drift	Hdg (t)	Var	Hdg (m)	Dev'	Hdg (C)	G/S	Dist	Time	ETA	REV ETA	ATA
KINGSWORTHY	OXFORD	2300	3500	359	12°s	347	4°W	351	0	351	88	44	30			

On Course:

EMERGENCY	121.5
RADIO FAIL	7600
MAYDAY	7700

IMP GALLONS	
AVGE USE	7 gph
TAXI T/O	2 + 2
TRIP	3½
APP LDG	2
RESERVE	7
MIN.REQ	16½
TOTAL FUEL ON	30
MAX. ENDURANCE	4 hrs

OBSERVATION

1	Railway between W'Church/Overton	+6
2	Newbury (South edge)	+12
3	O/h Abingdon A/D	+24

FACILITY	FREQ	
SOUTHAMPTON	118.2	tower
SOLENT	120.225	
BOSCOMBE DOWN	126.7	LARS
FARNBOROUGH	125.25	LARS
BENSON	120.9	LARS
BRIZE	134.3	LARS
OXFORD	125.325	ATC
	118.875	AFIS
THRUXTON	130.45	

THE PREPARED U.K. 1:500,000 CHART

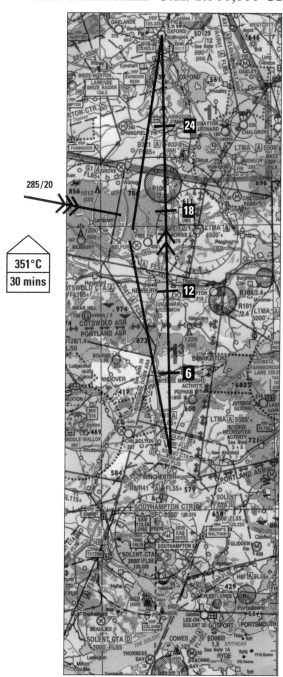

285/20

351°C

30 mins

Airborne Navigation

Or " The 64 million dollar question: does the plan work?"

You are now strapped into your 'Gentlemans aerial conveyance' and are ready for the off, armed with a plog, chart and a stopwatch. A wristwatch is also not a bad bit of kit to have, in addition to the stopwatch.

Why use a stopwatch? Well, you can very easily plan your flight times on the whizzwheel down to tenths of a minute with no hassle at all. Our planned groundspeed in this instance is 88 kt. It might easily have been as high as 120 kt. Even at the relatively slow speed of 88 kt, that is still 148 feet per second and this represents 888 feet in one tenth of a minute, or every 6 seconds. With a stopwatch you can easily time to the nearest tenth of a minute and so this is the ideal timing tool for accuracy whereas the wristwatch is good for coarse estimates of arrival time (ETA).

Let's pause for a moment and just cover a little more theory with respect to direction, since this is an appropriate point. Many people are content to navigate in magnetic and you will notice that so far, we have only calculated a magnetic heading. Your compass on board the aeroplane seeks magnetic north and so this appears to be a good proposition. Unfortunately, because the compass is set within a metal fuselage, surrounded by instruments, radios and headsets and is in the vicinity of the engine then the local magnetic field lines are deviated by all of this metal and by any other electro-magnetic fields within the aeroplane. Just try placing your headset near the compass and watch it swing. The upshot is that the compass has a potentially very large error. Since we are aware of this source of error then engineering will have 'swung' the compass for you, which is a term describing the process by which much of this error is eradicated. I say "much of this error" since there is usually a residual error left in the compass installation, although this should not exceed 3° in an aircraft where the compass is the sole heading reference.

Now despite their gruff and abrasive appearance outwardly, many 'engineering chappies' are really kind hearted souls deep down who do not like the thought of their 'pilot chappies' wandering around the sky, lost and confused and so they produce what is called a compass deviation card. This card is specific to a particular aircraft within a fleet and details the errors left on the compass every 30° or so. eg it will say "for 090°M, steer 091°C" meaning that in order to steer 090°, the compass will actually display 091° and hence there is a 'plus one degree' error on this heading. Therefore, on an easterly heading in that aeroplane, you would have to add one degree to your calculated magnetic heading to give a compass heading (°C) and it is this that you ultimately end up flying. This really is for the purists amongst us and in fact, most people tend to ignore this, whether by design or by ignorance!

Just occasionally the deviation is listed in terms of degrees east or west in much the same way as variation is. If this is the case then use a similar rhyme to that used for variation problems :-

   "Deviation WEST, Compass is BEST, Deviation EAST, Compass is LEAST"

So variation is the angular difference between true and magnetic headings and deviation is the angular difference between magnetic and compass headings. Clear?

Right, let's get airborne and go to work. For completeness on the plog, I have assumed that G-OPTC has a 0° error on northerly headings and so I have recorded this fact alongside of the compass heading of 351°C (351°M).

On the way to your navigation start point, in this case Kingsworthy, refresh your memory as to the required heading and the flight time. Arrange your flight so that you pass right overhead the start point on the desired heading and be careful that you have not built perhaps a quarter of a mile error into the equation by doing a 'sloppy overhead'. As you overfly the start point, set your stopwatch running and note the wristwatch time on your plog or chart. This is very important because it is ever so easy to knock the stopwatch and stop it.

The very next thing to do is what is called a 'gross error' check. This is designed to find large, stupid errors such as measuring your track with the protractor mis-aligned so that north becomes east for example, or you might accidentally set heading using the groundspeed! You would be amazed what I have seen! On a gross error check use the really big and obvious items first such as the sea being behind you and the position of the sun, which rises in the east and sets in the west. Many a pilot has pulled one out of the bag in this fashion! If there are no really gross errors then look for lesser problems. Am I going the correct way? Should that motorway on my left in fact be there, or should it have been to my right? Question everything.

If you are happy that there are no cock ups in the plan then afford yourself some confidence in the plan. Accept, for now, that the wind is as forecast (because even a perfect plan is only as good as this forecast) and fly the planned heading. A tip here that almost every PPL student and test candidate either forgets or ignores. Back in the early days of your training, do you remember the instructor telling you to look out of the window and to pick an aiming point ahead such that a heading could easily be maintained? Well do it then!! You will only hit the target by flying the heading, so fly the heading and leave the nav to me!

Once you have completed a gross error check and are steady on heading then your ETA (estimated time of arrival) should be calculated. This is achieved by adding the leg time to the noted departure time. Don't forget to mark this on your plog.

You have a good plan and you have checked that there are no gross errors. Have faith, fly the heading and throw the chart on to the back seat or sit on it! I'll say that again in case it is not clear enough. Throw the chart away; sit on it! Do anything with it except stare at it or fly with a finger on it! The chart is an unnecessary distraction to the important business of actually navigating! Too many people fly, staring at a chart and resting one finger on their present position lest they get lost! They look for little 'B' roads to corroborate their whereabouts and are constantly trying to update their present position. Because they are so preoccupied with not getting lost then they invariably do become lost. The heading wanders and the speed goes awry but they're OK, they have that magic finger on the chart showing where they are! That's not navigating - that's 'track-crawling' and is the surest way to going wrong in a hurry!

Expecting the plan to have been a reasonable one, you cannot err by very much within the short space of time of about six minutes and this just happens to be the time to your first fix point - the railway line between the two towns. Especially since you have just boosted your confidence by completing a gross error check. Your plan, good as it is, is only as good as the forecast wind however, so you might be slightly in error but I am willing to bet that you cannot go far enough wrong that you actually miss the fix point altogether. Clever, eh? So sit on your chart for maybe four of the six minutes and get on with the essential business of holding a steady heading, height and speed (don't forget the 90 kt IAS) and maintain a good lookout! (You are in the business of becoming an old, bold and bald pilot and you do this by not hitting other aeroplanes!). After four minutes then by all means pick up the chart and refresh your memory by glancing at the first fix. As I write I am conscious of being able to describe the fixes without my chart handy and this is because I have developed the knack of studying my route extensively pre-flight. I thus know the fixes and so, armed with a heading and a time, I could find Oxford without a chart, but don't try it! Maybe one day, I'll relate the story of how a cricket bat and a cherokee conspired to put me inside of the London Control Zone in marginal weather without a chart, but not yet!

When you are trying to locate a fix feature on the ground, remember to look well ahead of the aircraft; if you left it until you should be over the fix to start looking then that is far too late. It is amazing just how much ground that the engine cowling and wings can hide! Hence the reason why I advocate starting to look for the six minute feature after only four minutes have elapsed. Once you have identified your fix, it boils down to you deciding whether or not you are on track and thus whether or not you have to make a heading correction (track error plus the closing angle). Furthermore, you have to decide if your groundspeed is good or not; i.e. did you arrive at the fix on the planned time or were you early or late?

Timing errors may be of the 'once only' variety caused for example, by a climb or they maybe continually changing, caused by a stronger/weaker head or tail wind component. Do not be too hasty in revising your ETA but rather wait and look for the trend. In other words, if you arrive at the first fix on track but 30 seconds late then don't try to immediately change the ETA; rather you should expect to be at least 30 seconds late at the next point. If you are indeed 30 seconds late again, then you could now revise your ETA to some 30 seconds later. You have experienced a one-off timing error. However had the second fix arrived, say, 45 seconds late then you will begin to suspect an increasing error such as a stronger than anticipated headwind. You will now need to factor the error in order to produce an accurate ETA. eg 45 seconds late at the halfway point should, all things being equal, produce a minute and a half error at the destination. Try to keep these estimates simple as you will of course be flying the aeroplane as you try to do this. Instructors always appear to be such good navigators; they would - they're not flying!!!

FREDA checks should be done regularly and frequently and a very important feature here is the compass/direction indicator alignment. Only check this when you are straight and level in unaccelerated flight and make a particular point of doing this soon after a turning point. Many is the time that I have caused a good student to become unstuck because when they were very busy doing things in the cockpit I deliberately mis-aligned their D.I. Few picked this up because they were not doing regular enough FREDA checks!

Remember that when you are navigating solo, if it all goes wrong and you become hopelessly lost (and it's a horrible feeling, I can tell you) there is an abundance of radar units that are normally open for assistance and D&D (Distress and Diversion) assistance is always available 24 hours a day, 365 days a year. Use them. (In fact, get your instructor to arrange a practice emergency with them; pretend to be lost and see how good they are. The frequency is 121.5 MHZ and should be burned into the cortex of your brain!!

So the navigation emphasis is really on accurate and exhaustive planning followed by accurate flying in terms of heading and speed. Remember not to over map read and get used to consulting the chart just before a planned fix. Above all else, have confidence in your plan. Hopefully you will employ all of the little cross checks that I do along the way as I plan and these, allied with a gross error check on departure should eradicate all errors except those introduced by a bad wind forecast; and that is something, fellow navigator, over which you have no control. Happy navigating!!

LOST?!!

When I first envisaged writing this book I was actually arrogant enough to believe that I would not need to write about being lost in the air! Everybody would simply read my book and understand perfectly how they should navigate! Fortunately, I have matured somewhat in my ideas in the years that this project has taken to get off the ground and I have now decided that a few words here would probably go down very well. Actually, being lost and alone in the air is, I think, one of the steepest learning curves that the novitiate PPL can be expected to climb. I know, because I have been there. In my early days.

Funnily enough, most of my students that 'got lost' were not really genuinely lost at all. There was enough around them, on the ground, to fix their position. Indeed, many claimed to be lost when actually in sight of their destination! I can only assume that it was a sudden loss of confidence in their abilities and their navigation plan that led to a crisis in their thinking and leading them ultimately into declaring themselves lost. As soon as you believe that you are lost, then it almost invariably becomes effectively that.

Even if you are genuinely lost, there is always a logical reason as to why you are lost. What you as the pilot must do is to start thinking logically and resist the very common urge to start wandering in the air, haphazardly. Firstly, you have got to decide where you are. ("Where were you when you got lost?" "I don't know; otherwise I wouldn't be lost!!"). Seriously, look for features that stand out on the ground. Can you identify them on the chart? Take your intended track line on the chart and mark on it a rough position based on your predicted groundspeed. e.g. I have been flying for about 9 minutes at roughly 80 kt (say) - I should therefore be about 12 nm along the track line. Your 6 minute marks will come in handy here. Is there something nearby, on the chart that I perhaps could see out of the window?

Now that you have a rough position on the chart, if you still cannot find yourself then put a circle around that position of a radius equalling some 20% of the distance that you should have travelled in the time it has taken you to get lost. (About 2½ nm in our example). If you can't find yourself within this circle then gradually increase its diameter. All the time that you do this, you might consider making an orbit of your present position so that the error is not compounded while you think.

If these techniques fail to give you a clue as to your whereabouts then perhaps your error is more fundamental. Have you flown off on your groundspeed instead of your heading?! Stranger things have been done in the past! This is proof positive of the need for a good gross error check that I advocated as you set course.

Still unsure of what's going on? You're lost!! No doubt about it. Get help. Declare a PAN with either a LARS unit or on 121.5, the Distress and Diversion frequency.

Don't delay here. The sooner you ask for help, the quicker it will come and the danger of blundering , lost, into controlled airspace unannounced is reduced.

As I have already said, I got lost once. I was young, possibly overconfident and desperate for flying hours when I was asked to deliver an aeroplane from Cardiff to Goodwood. The weather was closing in but I thought that I could outrun it and so I launched. Halfway across the Bristol Channel I was down to 'scud-running' at low level; I had an IMC rating and could have climbed up through the weather but I had already started to mis-trust the VOR/ADF on board and so I elected to continue at low level. I was conscious of the high ground south of Bristol Airport and was mindful to stay clear to the south of this. The visibility was moderate to poor and I was beginning to realise the folly of my situation; track keeping was nigh on impossible at this low a level as I was having to make repeated diversions around villages and towns to remain legal. (As I said, I was inexperienced!). Eventually, a bright idea sprung into my head (the first that morning!) - if I headed a little south of south-east then I could ignore track crawling as I would soon pick up a railway line crossing my track, which not only went more or less in the right direction but it also took me towards lower lying ground (the white areas on the chart - remember the colour coding?). Sure enough, I did pick up a railway line, but it was whilst I was trying to ascertain exactly where it was that I had intersected that line that I realised there were in fact several railway lines, all in a close proximity and all travelling essentially the same direction for a short while! Which one had I picked up? Now I was in a quandary! I surmised that since railways go to places then if I followed this one it would lead me to somewhere that I might be able to identify. Shortly thereafter, I blundered across a village but I was unable to spot which one on the map. It was raining now, I was frightened and felt very alone. I was conscious that if I was on the wrong line then following it would leave me hopelessly and utterly lost. Solution? Eventually, my addled brain hit on the bright idea of calling for professional help in the guise of the local Naval Air Stations' radar (LARS). They replied that I was too low for a radar service but I think that the rising panic in my voice persuaded the man to fully tilt his scanner down and soon I was 'painting' on his screen and he was able to confirm which village I had been circling over for the last ten minutes. It did, in fact, confirm that I was right where I should have been and I was able to continue with renewed confidence on my way. Miraculously, minutes later I broke out ahead of the weather front and the rest of the flight was conducted at a sensible level and in serenity. My mistakes? Launching in the first place with dubious weather (press-on-itis) with dodgy nav. kit (so I was reluctant to climb and instrument fly) and not returning the moment I realised that I had goofed with the weather. On the plus side, I managed to utilise the resources available (radar) and I hit upon a sensible plan of action of following a line feature toward lower ground.

I hope that you are able to learn something from that little episode, as I certainly did. I am reminded of some advice that one of my instructors along the way once gave to me. He said, and I quote "Martyn, always learn from other pilots mistakes because you will never have enough time on this earth to make all of them yourself!!"

In Conclusion

Amazing isn't it? After all of those neat navigation calculations, after all of that preparation and the message that I have to say to you really boils down to 'keep those eyes wide open and fly in a straight line!' That is the way to do it, though - but who am I to tell you how to fly? Sure, go off and do it your own way but sooner or later you will probably realise that I am right and that what I have told you is the way to navigate visually. I've spent maybe 3000 of my 4000 hours doing it this way and I know it works! I also know that the skies over the United Kingdom are very busy and are consequently very dangerous (potentially) to you. When you navigate your attention is drawn a hundred different ways and maybe your lookout might just begin to suffer......you wont navigate anything like as effectively as you might with your head in the office and you are just waiting to become another collision statistic. Read again what I said about how to utilise your plan in the air and concentrate on flying straight and level at the correct airspeed on the right heading. Use reference points outside of the cockpit to maintain the desired course and then simply forget the navigation for the several minutes preceding your fix. Swivel that head and whilst you're at it, enjoy the scenery and the delight of flight!!

Many PPL students go wrong in their navigation because their planning was at fault. I hope that I have taught you the value of detailed planning on the ground - don't skimp on this; it is well over half of the battle. Others go wrong because although they might be carrying a good plan, they have the wrong attitude to flying. Don't get sloppy with your new-found flying skills. If you plan to fly at 3,500´ then consider it a personal sleight on your abilities if you are not within 50´ of that target. I had a wonderful Air Force Instructor who made me (a poor student) buy him pints if I was more than 50´ out or more than 5kt or 5° in error. I soon learned! (Thank you Kevin Lawry, if you ever read this!)

Another marvellous area for errors to arise comes when a pilot is getting confused with his navigation and he or she attempts to make what they actually see on the ground fit what they want to see from their charts. An example springs to mind when I had a student on a diversion from his planned leg towards Reading; his task was to go essentially southbound to overhead Popham and then to take us home to Southampton from there. Let's call him 'Mick' and leave it at that! He knows who I am talking about. So Mick gave me a good heading for Popham and at or about his ETA, Popham hove into view. Top marks, Mick! Now take me home! If you look at your chart you will realise what a simple task this could have been. Simply pick up the M3 motorway and follow southwards towards the edge of the Southampton CTR at Kingsworthy/Winchester. Mick was quite streetwise and duly (as expected) took about a nano-second to assimilate all of this (that's equivalent to the time it takes a QFI to put his wallet away when a student offers him a pint at the bar!). Unfortunately Mick did not put into place what was arguably the most important navigation trick I had ever taught him......(pin back your ears)..... a gross error check! His error was so gross that I find it difficult to talk about it..........oh, alright then....... he turned LEFT along the M3!! Not a problem, you might reasonably say. After a few minutes, when Winchester does not appear he will surely realise his mistake?! Not on your life! Basingstoke comes into view and is mistaken for Winchester! (It fits his plan - all apart from the fact that the conurbation lies to the left of the motorway and not to the right as would be the case at Winchester!). By now you might think that maybe I was being hard on Mick and should have pointed out the error in his ways. Not on your nelly! You see, he had already 'identified' the runway at RAF Odiham as being Southampton (his home base) despite the obvious things like a sadly lacking Solent or the City of Southampton itself not actually being there. I guess the moral here is that even an excellent, very simple plan can go wrong if you don't apply it correctly and you don't look for corroboration of its' validity with gross error checks.

I know that I keep harping on about this but all I really want to say, in conclusion, is plan thoroughly, extensively and carefully; fly accurately with regard to your parameters of height, heading and speed and keep a good look out!!

Oh, do practice your route planning as well. I believe that the publisher chappie is going to leave a few blank plogs for you to work from at the back of this book!!

Appendix 1

Measuring the track direction

Previously in the text, I gave you a rule that if you were navigating with a substantially easterly or westerly track then when it came to measuring the track angle with your protractor it should be done so at or around the tracks' midpoint. I promised an explanation.

If you remember, we obtain the direction of true north by reference to the meridians. Now when successive meridians cross the equator (that's the parallel of 0° latitude) they are parallel to each other. Grab a globe and verify this if you like. If you look at your chart, which is actually depicting a portion of the world at around 50° latitude, then these lines still appear to be parallel. Logic however, dictates that these meridians cannot be parallel because each meridian points to the north pole. All meridians meet at a point! It is only the scale of the chart, the sheer size of what we are trying to depict, that makes them appear to be parallel lines. Meridians must therefore lean towards each other and this is called convergency. Taking this argument one stage further, if you have a track line running say, west, then its' direction must be constantly changing with respect to the meridians as you cross each meridian. In other words, your track angle changes at a constant rate as you travel eastwards or westwards. Not that it is really important to you right now, but your straight line drawn on the chart represents the shortest distance between the two points and is an approximate great circle. Great circle navigation is marvellous in terms of being the shortest distance between two points but is problematical in terms of direction to us in our light aeroplane flying, with only our compass for direction keeping as we travel east or west.

Prove it; don't take my word for it. Take out your chart and draw a 'straight' track line from Lands End to Southend, or where ever else you desire east or west. Measure the track angle with respect to the local meridian at the start, the middle and the end of your track. You should begin to see that this track angle is not constant. Fascinating, n'est ce pas?

Hopefully you might just be cottoning on to a bijou problemette, which is my way of saying that "yes" there is a problem for you but pin back your ears, for I have a solution. The problem is of course, what on earth do you call your track direction for the purposes of a navigation calculation? How do we cope with a constantly changing track angle? We want a single track direction between Lands End and Southend so that we can work out in which direction to point the nose of our aeroplane.

The solution is elegant in its simplicity. Merely take the average track direction and perform your whizzwheel calculations on this. The average track between Lands

---

End and Southend is obtained by measuring the track line at or about its midpoint. That is to say, the middle meridian is used to align your protractor against. Hence my glib statement earlier that you measure tracks at their midpoints as a general rule. This is known as rhumb line navigation. (A rhumb line being a line on the chart of constant direction). With a rhumb line we can say the track direction is..... because it will be a set figure, constant in direction, although if you could draw it, it would appear as though it were a curved line bowing towards the equator slightly because of convergency.

For the purists amongst us then yes you will come south of track initially by flying the rhumb line direction but as you reach the halfway distance then the track direction that you are flying will be parallel to that drawn on the chart (because that was where it was measured). Maintaining your rhumb line direction will then cause you to gradually close up to the great circle (drawn) track, other things being equal. Finally, you will hit the same end point as that drawn on the chart. Obviously, since we have not flown the drawn great circle track but the average great circle, or rhumb track, then we will have flown slightly further than we had intended. However, calculation beyond the scope and remit of this book will show that, providing the track lines are less than 200 nm in length then this 'extra' distance involved is insignificant. So if you intend to fly a straight line track of say 1000 nm then I would wholeheartedly suggest breaking this down into five separate track lines of 200 nm in length and treating it as though you have a number of turning points en route. Measure each of these five track lines at their centre points and get on with it. You will naturally have to change course by a degree or so every 200 nm but that is a small price to pay for flying efficiently distance-wise.

A quick, sneaky tip. If your instructor starts whingeing about being south of track on an easterly or westerly track then smile sweetly and say "well that's convergency, aint it Guv?!!" Doubtless you will have him or her perplexed!

Appendix 2

The computer-heading solution amplified

On pages 34 and 38, whilst explaining how to use the computer, I made mention of a potential problem with a change in the drift as you turned the aeroplane. You may recall that, in our example, as you pointed to the target (i.e. heading = track) then the drift was established at 12°to the right. It didn't stretch the cerebrum too much, therefore, in electing to head some 12°to the left of track. This being based on the premise that, in pointing 12° to the left, the drift did not alter. Indeed, this was the case and more fool me for using this as an example!

Actually, the use of this example was quite deliberate to illustrate to you an important navigational point and a useful crosscheck. The point is this - if, at the end of the day the difference between the heading and your track does not equal the drift then you might as well give up and go home because you certainly will not fly along your intended track. In our example 347° + 12° = 359°, which is the intended track and so everything is hunky-dory.

Consider our Oxford trip again but this time the forecast wind is now 240°/20 kt. The track is still 359° (obviously!) and the TAS is still 95kt. As before, mark your wind on the computer and set in the TAS. Ignore the wind and point the aeroplane at Oxford by rotating your computer to the track direction of 359° and read the drift. I make this 9° to the right and hence I would compensate for this by turning 9° to the left. (The 'Martyn Smith' method is to say drift right-right thumb down for 9°). The computer should now read 350° and you might expect that this is your heading to fly. WRONG!! Read off your drift currently being experienced on a heading of 350°. Heavens above!! It's 10°! Now 350°+ 10° = 360° and not the desired 359°. You have turned more into wind and the drift has increased.

The solution is fairly straightforward. When you have made your initial allowance for the drift then you always re-check the drift. If it has not changed then you have the correct solution. If, however, it has changed by, say, increasing then you have not allowed enough and you should increase your allowance by the amount of the change.

Thus, in our last example, where the initial drift estimate was 9° and then became 10° you should turn a further 1° so that you are now displaying 349° on the computer. Again, re-check the current drift on 349°. Ah, it has remained at 10° to the right. Bingo! A navigators crosscheck confirms that the 349° heading with 10° right drift will give a track of 359°. This is called "balancing the drift". It is an iterative process which might have to be repeated a couple of times until the drift balances to give the correct track.

If you are in a position where your drift decreases after your turn (instead of an increase as we previously saw) then you simply follow by decreasing or reducing the amount of drift that you lay off by an amount equalling the change.

As long as, at the end of the day, you have a heading ± drift = track then you have the correct solution.

ASCO VFR FLIGHT LOG

DEPARTURE		ARRIVAL
FIELD		
R/W		
QFE		
QNH		
WIND		

CALL SIGN	
PILOT	

AREA	QNH	QNH

WEATHER	W/V	TEMP	IAS	TAS

CHX OFF	T/O	LAND	CHX ON

W X

FROM	TO	MSA	Alt	Trk (t)	Drift	Hdg (t)	Var	Hdg (m)	Dev'	Hdg (c)	G/S	Dist	Time	ETA	REV ETA	ATA

FACILITY	FREQ

EMERGENCY	121.5
RADIO FAIL	7600
MAYDAY	7700

IMP GALLONS	
AVGE USE	
TAXI T/O	
TRIP	
APP LDG	
RESERVE	
MIN.REQ	
TOTAL FUEL ON	
MAX. ENDURANCE	

OBSERVATION

ASCO VFR FLIGHT LOG

WEATHER	W/V	TEMP	IAS	TAS

CHX OFF	T/O	LAND	CHX ON

	DEPARTURE	ARRIVAL
FIELD		
R/W		
QFE		
QNH		
WIND		
W X		

CALL SIGN	
PILOT	

AREA	QNH	QNH

FROM	TO	MSA	Alt	Trk (t)	Drift	Hdg (t)	Var	Hdg (m)	Dev'	Hdg (c)	G/S	Dist	Time	ETA	REV ETA	ATA

EMERGENCY	121.5
RADIO FAIL	7600
MAYDAY	7700

IMP GALLONS	
AVGE USE	
TAXI T/O	
TRIP	
APP LDG	
RESERVE	
MIN.REQ	
TOTAL FUEL ON	
MAX. ENDURANCE	

FACILITY	FREQ

OBSERVATION

ASCO VFR FLIGHT LOG

WEATHER	W/V	TEMP	IAS	TAS

CALL SIGN	
PILOT	

	DEPARTURE	ARRIVAL
FIELD		
R/W		
QFE		
QNH		
WIND		
W X		

CHX OFF	T/O	LAND	CHX ON

AREA	QNH	QNH

FROM	TO	MSA	Alt	Trk (t)	Drift	Hdg (t)	Var	Hdg (m)	Dev'	Hdg (c)	G/S	Dist	Time	ETA	REV ETA	ATA

FACILITY	FREQ

EMERGENCY	121.5
RADIO FAIL	7600
MAYDAY	7700

IMP GALLONS	
AVGE USE	
TAXI T/O	
TRIP	
APP LDG	
RESERVE	
MIN.REQ	
TOTAL FUEL ON	
MAX. ENDURANCE	

OBSERVATION

ASCO VFR FLIGHT LOG

WEATHER	W/V	TEMP	IAS	TAS

CHX OFF	T/O	LAND	CHX ON

CALL SIGN		
PILOT		

AREA	QNH	QNH

	DEPARTURE	ARRIVAL
FIELD		
R/W		
QFE		
QNH		
WIND		
W X		

FROM	TO	MSA	Alt	Trk (t)	Drift	Hdg (t)	Var	Hdg (m)	Dev'	Hdg (c)	G/S	Dist	Time	ETA	REV ETA	ATA

FACILITY	FREQ

EMERGENCY	121.5
RADIO FAIL	7600
MAYDAY	7700

IMP GALLONS	
AVGE USE	
TAXI T/O	
TRIP	
APP LDG	
RESERVE	
MIN.REQ	
TOTAL FUEL ON	
MAX. ENDURANCE	

OBSERVATION

ASCO VFR FLIGHT LOG

WEATHER	W/V	TEMP	IAS	TAS

CHX OFF	T/O	LAND	CHX ON

CALL SIGN	
PILOT	

AREA	QNH	QNH

	DEPARTURE	ARRIVAL
FIELD		
R/W		
QFE		
QNH		
WIND		
W X		

FROM	TO	MSA	Alt	Trk (t)	Drift	Hdg (t)	Var	Hdg (m)	Dev'	Hdg (c)	G/S	Dist	Time	ETA	REV ETA	ATA

FACILITY	FREQ

EMERGENCY	121.5
RADIO FAIL	7600
MAYDAY	7700

IMP GALLONS	
AVGE USE	
TAXI T/O	
TRIP	
APP LDG	
RESERVE	
MIN.REQ	
TOTAL FUEL ON	
MAX. ENDURANCE	

OBSERVATION